Financial Accounting Fundamentals Working Papers

3rd Edition

Contains Material from

Financial & Managerial Accounting
Information For Decisions
Fourth Edition
Volume 1, Chapters 1-13

John J. Wild
University of Wisconsin at Madison

Ken W. Shaw
University of Missouri at Columbia

Barbara Chiappetta
Nassau Community College

CSN
COLLEGE OF
SOUTHERN NEVADA

 Learning Solutions

Boston   Burr Ridge, IL   Dubuque, IA   New York   San Francisco
St. Louis Bangkok Bogotá Caracas Lisbon London Madrid
Mexico City Milan New Delhi Seoul Singapore Sydney Taipei Toronto

FINANCIAL ACCOUNTING FUNDAMENTALS, THIRD EDITION
WORKING PAPERS
College of Southern Nevada

Copyright © 2011 by The McGraw-Hill Companies, Inc. All rights reserved. Printed in the United States of America. Except as permitted under the United States Copyright Act of 1976, no part of this publication may be reproduced or distributed in any form or by any means, or stored in a data base retrieval system, without prior written permission of the publisher.

This book is a McGraw-Hill Learning Solutions textbook and contains select material from *Financial and Managerial Accounting: Information for Decisions, Volume 1, Chapters 1-13,* Fourth Edition by John J. Wild, Ken W. Shaw and Barbara Chiappetta. Copyright © 2011, 2009, 2007, 2005 by The McGraw-Hill Companies, Inc. Reprinted with permission of the publisher. Many custom published texts are modified versions or adaptations of our best-selling textbooks. Some adaptations are printed in black and white to keep prices at a minimum, while others are in color.

1 2 3 4 5 6 7 8 9 0   DOW DOW   13 12 11

ISBN-13: 978-0-07-756073-7
ISBN-10: 0-07-756073-6

Learning Solutions Manager: Terri Harvey
Production Editor: Jessica Portz
Printer/Binder: RR Donnelley - Willard

TABLE OF CONTENTS

Chapter

Appendices

Name _____

(a) & (b)

GAAP: _____
Importance: _____
_____
_____

SEC: _____
Importance: _____
_____
_____
_____

FASB: _____
Importance: _____
_____
_____

IASB: _____
Importance: _____
_____
_____

IFRS: _____
Importance: _____
_____
_____
_____

Quick Study 1-2

_____
_____
_____
_____
_____
_____
_____
_____
_____

Name _____

(a) _____   (g) _____
(b) _____   (h) _____
(c) _____   (i) _____
(d) _____   (j) _____
(e) _____   (k) _____
(f) _____   (l) _____

Quick Study 1-4

(1) _____
_____
_____

(2) _____
_____
_____

(3) _____
_____
_____

(4) _____
_____
_____

Quick Study 1-5

_____
_____
_____
_____
_____
_____
_____
_____

(a) _____

(b) _____

(c) _____

Quick Study 1-7

Assets	=	Liabilities	+	Equity
(a)				
(b)				

Quick Study 1-8

Assets	=	Liabilities	+	Equity
$ 30,000		(a) _____		$20,000
(b) _____		$50,000		$30,000
$ 90,000		$10,000		(c) _____

Business transactions: _____

_____
_____
_____

Business events: _____

_____
_____
_____

Quick Study 1-10

(a) (1) _____
   (2) _____
   (3) _____

(b)	Assets	=	Liabilities	+	Equity
		=		+	

Quick Study 1-11

Return on Assets: _____

_____
_____

Interpretation: _____

_____
_____

Quick Study 1-12

(a) _____	(d) _____	(g) _____
(b) _____	(e) _____	(h) _____
(c) _____	(f) _____	(i) _____

Quick Study 1-13

a. _____

b. _____

c. _____

Chapter 1   Exercise 1-1   Name _____

(1) _____   (5) _____
(2) _____   (6) _____
(3) _____   (7) _____
(4) _____

Exercise 1-2

Part A

(1) _____   (5) _____
(2) _____   (6) _____
(3) _____   (7) _____
(4) _____   (8) _____

Part B

(1) _____   (5) _____
(2) _____   (6) _____
(3) _____   (7) _____
(4) _____

Exercise 1-3

(1) _____   (5) _____
(2) _____   (6) _____
(3) _____   (7) _____
(4) _____   (8) _____

(a) _____

_____

_____

(b) _____

_____

_____

(c) _____

_____

_____

(d) _____

_____

_____

Exercise 1-5

(1) _____
(2) _____
(3) _____
(4) _____
(5) _____

Exercise 1-6

(1) _____
(2) _____
(3) _____
(4) _____
(5) _____
(6) _____
(7) _____
(8) _____

Exercise 1-7

(a) _____
(b) _____
(c) _____
(d) _____
(e) _____
(f) _____
(g) _____

(a) _____

_____

_____

_____

(b) _____

_____

_____

_____

_____

_____

_____

_____

(c) _____

_____

_____

_____

_____

_____

_____

_____

Exercise 1-9

Assets	=	Liabilities	+	Equity

(a) _____

(b) _____

(c) _____

(a) _____

_____

(b) _____

_____

(c) _____

_____

(d) _____

_____

(e) _____

_____

(f) _____

_____

(g) _____

_____

Exercise 1-11

Cash	+	Accounts Receivable	+	Equipment	=	Accounts Payable	+	Common Stock	-	Dividends	+	Revenues	-	Expenses
(a)														
Bal.														
(b)														
Bal.														
(c)														
Bal.														
(d)														
Bal.														
(e)														
Bal.														
(f)														
Bal.														
(g)														
Bal.														
(h)														
Bal.														
(i)														
Bal.														
(j)														
Bal.														

(a) _____
_____

(b) _____
_____

(c) _____
_____

(d) _____
_____

(e) _____
_____

Exercise 1-13

(a) _____
_____

(b) _____
_____

(c) _____
_____

(d) _____
_____

(e) _____
_____

Income Statement

Exercise 1-15

Statement of Retained Earnings

Balance Sheet

Exercise 1-17

Statement of Cash Flows

Name _____

Return on Assets: _____

_____

_____

_____

Interpretation: _____

_____

_____

Exercise 1-19

(1) _____   (5) _____

(2) _____   (6) _____

(3) _____   (7) _____

(4) _____   (8) _____

Exercise 1-20[B]

(1) _____

(2) _____

(3) _____

(4) _____

(5) _____

Exercise 1-21

_____

_____

Income Statement

_____

_____

_____

_____

_____

_____

_____

_____

TRANSACTION	Balance Sheet			Income Stmt.	Statement of Cash Flows		
	TOTAL ASSETS	TOTAL LIABILITIES	TOTAL EQUITY	NET INCOME	OPERATING ACTIVITIES	FINANCING ACTIVITIES	INVESTING ACTIVITIES
1.							
2.							
3.							
4.							
5.							
6.							
7.							
8.							
9.							
10.							

Part 1: Company_____

(a) _____
_____
_____
_____
_____

(b) _____
_____
_____
_____
_____
_____
_____

(c) _____
_____
_____
_____
_____

Part 2: Company_____

(a) _____
_____

(b) _____
_____

(c) _____
_____
_____
_____
_____

Part 3: Company_____

_____
_____
_____
_____
_____
_____
_____
_____
_____
_____
_____
_____
_____
_____
_____
_____
_____
_____
_____

Part 4: Company_____

_____
_____
_____
_____
_____
_____
_____
_____
_____
_____
_____
_____
_____
_____
_____
_____

Part 5: Company_____

_____
_____
_____
_____
_____
_____
_____
_____
_____
_____
_____
_____
_____
_____
_____
_____

_____

Balance Sheet

===
_____
_____
_____
_____
_____
_____

Problem 1-4A or 1-4B

_____

Income Statement

===
_____
_____
_____
_____
_____

Problem 1-5A or 1-5B

_____

Statement of Retained Earnings

===
_____
_____
_____
_____
_____

_____

Statement of Cash Flows

_____

Parts 1 & 2

	ASSESTS						LIABILITIES			EQUITY			
CASH	+ ACCOUNTS RECEIVABLE	+ OFFICE SUPPLIES	+ OFFICE EQUIPMENT	+ BUILDING	=	ACCOUNTS PAYABLE	+ NOTES PAYABLE	+ COMMON STOCK	- DIVIDENDS	+ REVENUES	- EXPENSES		
a.													
b.													
Bal.													
c.													
Bal.													
d.													
Bal.													
e.													
Bal.													
f.													
Bal.													
g.													
Bal.													
h.													
Bal.													
i.													
Bal.													
j.													
Bal.													
k.													
Bal.													

Part 3

_____

_____

_____

Name _____

Parts 1 & 2

	ASSETS			=	LIABILITIES +		EQUITY			
DATE	CASH	+ ACCOUNTS RECEIVABLE	+ EQUIPMENT	=	ACCOUNTS PAYABLE	+ COMMON STOCK	- DIVIDENDS	+ REVENUES	- EXPENSES

Income Statement

Statement of Retained Earnings

Balance Sheet

Statement of Cash Flows

Name _____

DATE	ASSETS				= LIABILITIES	+	EQUITY				
	CASH	+ ACCOUNTS RECEIVABLE	+ OFFICE SUPPLIES	+ OFFICE EQUIPMENT	+ EQUIPMENT	= ACCOUNTS PAYABLE	+ COMMON STOCK	- DIVIDENDS	+ REVENUES	- EXPENSES

Income Statement

Statement of Retained Earnings

Balance Sheet

Statement of Cash Flows

Part 4

(1)

_____

_____

(2)

_____

_____

(3)

_____

_____

(4)

_____

_____

_____

Problem 1-11A or 1-11B

(1a)

_____

(1b)

_____

_____

(2)

_____

_____

(3)

_____

_____

(4)

_____

_____

_____

_____

(1) Return: _____
_____

Risk: _____
_____

(2) Return: _____
_____

Risk: _____
_____

(3) Return: _____
_____

Risk: _____
_____

(4) Return: _____
_____

Risk: _____
_____

Chapter 1   Problem 1-13A^B   *Name* _____

(1) Major Activity: _____

_____

_____

(2) Major Activity: _____

_____

_____

(3) Major Activity: _____

_____

_____

Problem 1-13B^B

I. _____

   A. _____

   B. _____

II. _____

   A. _____

   B. _____

III. _____

   A. _____

   B. _____

Problem 1-14A^B or 1-14B^B

(1) _____	(5) _____
(2) _____	(6) _____
(3) _____	(7) _____
(4) _____	(8) _____

Chapter 1

Serial Problem, SP 1
Business Solutions

Name _____

	ASSETS					LIABILITIES	EQUITY				
DATE	CASH +	ACCOUNTS RECEIVABLE +	COMPUTER SUPPLIES +	COMPUTER SYSTEM +	OFFICE EQUIPMENT =	ACCOUNTS PAYABLE +	COMMON STOCK -	DIVIDENDS	+ REVENUES	- EXPENSES
Oct. 1										
Oct. 3										
Bal.										
Oct. 6										
Bal.										
Oct. 8										
Bal.										
Oct. 12										
Bal.										
Oct. 15										
Bal.										
Oct. 17										
Bal.										
Oct. 20										
Bal.										
Oct. 22										
Bal.										
Oct. 28										
Bal.										
Oct. 31										
Bal.										
Oct. 31										
Bal.										

(1) _____
_____
_____
_____

(2) _____
_____
_____
_____
_____

(3) _____
_____
_____
_____
_____

(4) _____
_____
_____
_____
_____

(5) FastForward: _____
_____
_____
_____

Research In Motion	Apple
(1)	
(2)	
(3)	
(4)	
(5)	

Ethics Challenge—BTN 1-3

(1) _____

_____

_____

(2) _____

_____

_____

(3) _____

_____

_____

(4) _____

_____

_____

(1) **—Request For Information—**

(2) _____

1. _____
_____
_____
_____
_____
_____
_____

2. _____
_____
_____
_____

Teamwork in Action—BTN 1-6

(1) **Meeting Time and Place:**   _____
_____

(2) **Telephone and E-mail Addresses:**   _____
_____
_____
_____
_____

Instructor Notification: ☐ **YES** _____

(1)(a) _____

_____

_____

_____

_____

(b) _____

_____

_____

_____

_____

(2) _____

_____

_____

_____

_____

_____

_____

(1) _____
_____
_____
_____
_____

(2) _____
_____
_____
_____
_____

(3) _____
_____
_____
_____
_____

Global Decision—BTN 1-9

(1) _____
_____
_____
_____
_____
_____

(2) _____
_____
_____
_____
_____
_____

(a) _____   (f) _____
(b) _____   (g) _____
(c) _____   (h) _____
(d) _____   (i) _____
(e) _____

Quick Study 2-2

Likely source documents are: _____

_____

_____

_____

_____

Quick Study 2-3

(a) _____   (f) _____
(b) _____   (g) _____
(c) _____   (h) _____
(d) _____   (i) _____
(e) _____   (j) _____

Quick Study 2-4

(a) _____   (f) _____
(b) _____   (g) _____
(c) _____   (h) _____
(d) _____   (i) _____
(e) _____

Quick Study 2-5

(a) _____   (g) _____
(b) _____   (h) _____
(c) _____   (i) _____
(d) _____   (j) _____
(e) _____   (k) _____
(f) _____   (l) _____

GENERAL JOURNAL

Date		Account Titles and Explanation	PR	Debit	Credit

Quick Study 2-7

Answer: _____

Explanation: _____
_____
_____

Quick Study 2-8

(a) _____	(g) _____
(b) _____	(h) _____
(c) _____	(i) _____
(d) _____	(j) _____
(e) _____	(k) _____
(f) _____	(l) _____

(a) _____
_____

(b) _____
_____
_____
_____

(c) _____
_____
_____
_____
_____

Exercise 2-1

_____ a. Record relevant transactions in a journal
_____ b. Prepare and analyze the trial balance
_____ c. Analyze each transaction from source documents
_____ d. Post journal information to ledger accounts

Exercise 2-2

a. _____
b. _____
c. _____
d. _____
e. _____

Exercise 2-3

a. _____
b. _____

ACCOUNT	TYPE OF ACCOUNT	NORMAL BALANCE	INCREASE (Dr. or Cr.)
a.			
b.			
c.			
d.			
e.			
f.			
g.			
h.			
i.			
j.			
k.			
l.			

Exercise 2-5

_____
_____
_____
_____
_____
_____
_____
_____
_____
_____
_____
_____
_____
_____
_____
_____

(1)
_____
_____
_____
_____
_____
_____
_____

(2)
_____
_____
_____
_____
_____
_____
_____

(3)
_____
_____
_____
_____
_____
_____
_____

GENERAL JOURNAL

Date		Account Titles and Explanation	PR	Debit	Credit

Cash	**Photography Equipment**
Office Supplies	**Common Stock**
Prepaid Insurance	**Photography Fees Earned**
	Utilities Expense

Trial Balance

GENERAL JOURNAL

Date	Account Titles and Explanation	PR	Debit	Credit

Name _____

Transactions creating expenses and their entries:

GENERAL JOURNAL

Date	Account Titles and Explanation	PR	Debit	Credit

Transactions not creating expenses and the reasons: _____

_____

_____

_____

_____

_____

_____

_____

_____

_____

_____

_____

_____

_____

Income Statement

Exercise 2-14

Statement of Retained Earnings

Balance Sheet

(a) Net Income (Loss) = ▭
     Supporting Computations: _____

_____

_____

_____

_____

_____

_____

_____

(b) Net Income (Loss) = ▭
     Supporting Computations: _____

_____

_____

_____

_____

_____

_____

_____

(c) Net Income (Loss) = ▭
     Supporting Computations: _____

_____

_____

_____

_____

_____

_____

(d) Net Income (Loss) = ▭
     Supporting Computations: _____

_____

_____

_____

_____

_____

_____

_____

	(a)	(b)	(c)	(d)

Exercise 2-18

(a) _____

(b) _____

(c) _____

(d) _____

(e) _____

(f) _____

(g) _____

GENERAL JOURNAL

Date	Account Titles and Explanation	PR	Debit	Credit
(a)				
(b)				
(c)				
(d)				
(e)				
(f)				
(g)				

	Description	(1) Difference between Debit and Credit Columns	(2) Column with the Larger Total	(3) Identify account(s) incorrectly stated	(4) Amount that account(s) is overstated or understated
(a)	$2,400 debit to Rent Expense is posted as a $1,590 debit.	$810	Credit	Rent Expense	Rent Expense is understated by $810
(b)					
(c)					
(d)					
(e)					
(f)					
(g)					

Chapter 2   Exercise 2-21   Name _____

(a) _____
_____
_____

(b) _____
_____
_____

(c) _____
_____
_____

(d) _____
_____
_____

(e) _____
_____
_____

Part 2

Net Income Computation: _____
_____
_____
_____
_____
_____
_____
_____
_____
_____
_____
_____

Part 3

Debt Ratio: _____
_____
_____
_____
_____

Part 1

GENERAL JOURNAL

Date	Account Titles and Explanation	PR	Debit	Credit

Date		Account Titles and Explanation	PR	Debit	Credit

Part 2

GENERAL LEDGER

Cash   ACCOUNT NO. 101

Date	Explanation	PR	DEBIT	CREDIT	BALANCE

Accounts Receivable   ACCOUNT NO. 106

Date	Explanation	PR	DEBIT	CREDIT	BALANCE

Office Supplies   ACCOUNT NO. 124

Date	Explanation	PR	DEBIT	CREDIT	BALANCE

Prepaid Insurance   ACCOUNT NO. 128

Date	Explanation	PR	DEBIT	CREDIT	BALANCE

Prepaid Rent   **ACCOUNT NO. 131**

Date	Explanation	PR	DEBIT	CREDIT	BALANCE

Office Equipment   **ACCOUNT NO. 163**

Date	Explanation	PR	DEBIT	CREDIT	BALANCE

Accounts Payable   **ACCOUNT NO. 201**

Date	Explanation	PR	DEBIT	CREDIT	BALANCE

Common Stock   **ACCOUNT NO. 307**

Date	Explanation	PR	DEBIT	CREDIT	BALANCE

Dividends   **ACCOUNT NO. 319**

Date	Explanation	PR	DEBIT	CREDIT	BALANCE

Service Fees Earned**				ACCOUNT NO. 401	
Date	Explanation	PR	DEBIT	CREDIT	BALANCE

Services Revenue*				ACCOUNT NO. 403	
Date	Explanation	PR	DEBIT	CREDIT	BALANCE

Utilities Expense				ACCOUNT NO. 690	
Date	Explanation	PR	DEBIT	CREDIT	BALANCE

* Problem 2-4A only.
** Problem 2-4B only.

Trial Balance

Part 1

GENERAL JOURNAL

Date	Account Titles and Explanation	PR	Debit	Credit

Date	Account Titles and Explanation	PR	Debit	Credit

Part 2

Cash   No. 101

DATE	PR	Debit	Credit	Balance

Accounts Receivable   No. 106

DATE	PR	Debit	Credit	Balance

Office Supplies   No. 108

DATE	PR	Debit	Credit	Balance

Office Equipment   No. 163

DATE	PR	Debit	Credit	Balance

Automobiles   No. 164

DATE	PR	Debit	Credit	Balance

Building   No. 170

DATE	PR	Debit	Credit	Balance

Land   No. 172

DATE	PR	Debit	Credit	Balance

Accounts Payable   No. 201

DATE	PR	Debit	Credit	Balance

Notes Payable   No. 250

DATE	PR	Debit	Credit	Balance

Common Stock   No. 307

DATE	PR	Debit	Credit	Balance

Dividends   No. 319

DATE	PR	Debit	Credit	Balance

Fees Earned   No. 402

DATE	PR	Debit	Credit	Balance

Salaries Expense   No. 601

DATE	PR	Debit	Credit	Balance

Utilities Expense   No. 602

DATE	PR	Debit	Credit	Balance

Part 3

Trial Balance

Part 1

_____

Trial Balance

_____

_____

Part 2

Seven Most Likely Transactions (following order of trial balance):

(1) _____

(2) _____

(3) _____

(4) _____

(5) _____

(6) _____

(7) _____

Part 3

Report of Cash Received and Cash Paid

Part 1

GENERAL JOURNAL

Date	Account Titles and Explanation	PR	Debit	Credit

Date		Account Titles and Explanation	PR	Debit	Credit

Date	Account Titles and Explanation	PR	Debit	Credit

Part 2

GENERAL LEDGER

Cash   ACCOUNT NO. 101

Date	Explanation	PR	DEBIT	CREDIT	BALANCE

Accounts Receivable   ACCOUNT NO. 106

Date	Explanation	PR	DEBIT	CREDIT	BALANCE

Computer Supplies   ACCOUNT NO. 126

Date	Explanation	PR	DEBIT	CREDIT	BALANCE

Prepaid Insurance   ACCOUNT NO. 128

Date	Explanation	PR	DEBIT	CREDIT	BALANCE

Prepaid Rent   ACCOUNT NO. 131

Date	Explanation	PR	DEBIT	CREDIT	BALANCE

Office Equipment   ACCOUNT NO. 163

Date	Explanation	PR	DEBIT	CREDIT	BALANCE

Computer Equipment   ACCOUNT NO. 167

Date	Explanation	PR	DEBIT	CREDIT	BALANCE

Accounts Payable — ACCOUNT NO. 201

Date	Explanation	PR	DEBIT	CREDIT	BALANCE

Common Stock — ACCOUNT NO. 307

Date	Explanation	PR	DEBIT	CREDIT	BALANCE

Dividends — ACCOUNT NO. 319

Date	Explanation	PR	DEBIT	CREDIT	BALANCE

Computer Services Revenue — ACCOUNT NO. 403

Date	Explanation	PR	DEBIT	CREDIT	BALANCE

Chapter 2   Serial Problem, SP 2   Name _____
             Business Solutions

Part 2   (Continued)

Wages Expense   ACCOUNT NO. 623

Date	Explanation	PR	DEBIT	CREDIT	BALANCE

Advertising Expense   ACCOUNT NO. 655

Date	Explanation	PR	DEBIT	CREDIT	BALANCE

Mileage Expense   ACCOUNT NO. 676

Date	Explanation	PR	DEBIT	CREDIT	BALANCE

Miscellaneous Expense   ACCOUNT NO. 677

Date	Explanation	PR	DEBIT	CREDIT	BALANCE

Repairs Expense-Computer   ACCOUNT NO. 684

Date	Explanation	PR	DEBIT	CREDIT	BALANCE

Part 3

Trial Balance

(1) _____

_____

_____

(2) _____

_____

_____

(3) _____

_____

_____

_____

(4) _____

_____

_____

_____

(5) FastForward: _____

_____

_____

_____

_____

_____

(1) Current Year Debt Ratio: _____

_____

Prior Year Debt Ratio: _____

_____

_____

(2) Current Year Debt Ratio: _____

_____

Prior Year Debt Ratio: _____

_____

_____

(3) _____

_____

_____

_____

_____

_____

_____

_____

Ethics Challenge—BTN 2-3

_____

_____

_____

_____

_____

_____

_____

_____

_____

_____

_____

_____

_____

_____

MEMORANDUM

TO:

FROM:

SUBJECT:

DATE:

---

(1) _____
_____
_____
_____
_____
_____
_____

(2) _____
_____
_____
_____
_____
_____
_____

(3) _____
_____
_____
_____
_____
_____
_____

(1) Component selected: _____

(2) (a) _____
_____

   (b) _____
_____

   (c) _____
_____

   (d) _____
_____

   (e) _____
_____

(3) Presentation Notes:
_____
_____
_____
_____
_____
_____

_____
_____
_____
_____
_____
_____
_____
_____
_____
_____
_____
_____
_____

(1) _____

Balance Sheet

_____
_____
_____
_____
_____
_____
_____
_____
_____
_____
_____
_____
_____
_____

(2) _____

_____
_____
_____
_____
_____
_____
_____
_____
_____
_____

(3) _____

_____
_____
_____
_____
_____
_____
_____
_____

(1) _____

_____

_____

_____

_____

_____

(2) _____

_____

_____

_____

_____

_____

(3) _____

_____

_____

_____

_____

(4) _____

_____

_____

_____

_____

_____

(1) _____
_____
_____
_____

(2) _____
_____
_____
_____

(3) _____
_____
_____
_____

(a) _____

(b) _____

(c) _____

(d) _____

(e) _____

Quick Study 3-2

GENERAL JOURNAL

Date	Account Titles and Explanation	PR	Debit	Credit
(a)				
(b)				

Quick Study 3-3

GENERAL JOURNAL

Date	Account Titles and Explanation	PR	Debit	Credit
(a)				
(b)				

GENERAL JOURNAL

Date		Account Titles and Explanation	PR	Debit	Credit
(a)					
(b)					

Quick Study 3-5

GENERAL JOURNAL

Date		Account Titles and Explanation	PR	Debit	Credit

(a)

Dr./Cr.	Account Titles	Financial Statement
Debit		
Credit		

(b)

Debit		
Credit		

(c)

Debit		
Credit		

(d)

Debit		
Credit		

(e)

Debit		
Credit		

Quick Study 3-7

Cash Basis

_____

_____

_____

_____

_____

Accrual Basis

_____

_____

_____

_____

_____

Answer is _____
Supporting work:

_____

_____

_____

_____

Quick Study 3-9

Answer is _____
Supporting work:

_____

_____

_____

_____

_____

Quick Study 3-10

Adjustment	Debit	Credit
(1)		
(2)		
(3)		

Profit Margin:

_____

_____

_____

_____

Interpretation of Profit Margin:

_____

_____

_____

_____

_____

Quick Study 3-12^A

Answer is _____

Supporting work: _____

_____

_____

_____

Quick Study 3-13

a. _____

b. _____

_____

Steps

1st	_____
2nd	_____
3rd	_____
4th	_____
5th	_____
6th	_____
7th	_____
8th	_____
9th	_____

Quick Study 3-15

Current Ratio: _____

_____

_____

_____

_____

_____

_____

_____

_____

Quick Study 3-16

(1) _____	(5) _____
(2) _____	(6) _____
(3) _____	(7) _____
(4) _____	(8) _____

Name _____

GENERAL JOURNAL

Date	Account Titles and Explanation	PR	Debit	Credit

Quick Study 3-18

_____

_____

_____

_____

_____ Company

_____ Work Sheet

ACCOUNT TITLE	Unadjusted Trial Balance		Adjustments		Adjusted Trial Balance		Income Statement		Balance Sheet	
	Dr.	Cr.	Dr.	Cr.	Dr.	Cr.	Dr.	Cr.	Dr.	Cr.
Prepaid rent										
Services revenue										
Wages expense										
Accounts receivable										
Wages payable										
Rent expense										

GENERAL JOURNAL

Date		Account Titles and Explanation	PR	Debit	Credit

GENERAL JOURNAL

Date	Account Titles and Explanation	PR	Debit	Credit
(a)				
(b)				
(c)				
(d)				
(e)				
(f)				
(g)				

Notes: _____

_____

_____

_____

GENERAL JOURNAL

Date	Account Titles and Explanation	PR	Debit	Credit
(a)				
(b)				
(c)				
(d)				
(e)				
(f)				

Notes: _____

_____

_____

_____

Chapter 3   Exercise 3-3   *Name* _____

(a)

GENERAL JOURNAL

Date	Account Titles and Explanation	PR	Debit	Credit
Adjusting Entry:				
Journal Entry (Next Period):				

(b)

GENERAL JOURNAL

Date	Account Titles and Explanation	PR	Debit	Credit
Adjusting Entry:				
Journal Entry (Next Period):				

(c)

GENERAL JOURNAL

Date	Account Titles and Explanation	PR	Debit	Credit
Adjusting Entry:				
Journal Entry (Next Period):				

a. Answer: _____

  Supporting Work: _____

_____

_____

b. Answer: _____

  Supporting Work: _____

_____

_____

c. Answer: _____

  Supporting Work: _____

_____

_____

d. Answer: _____

  Supporting Work: _____

_____

_____

Exercise 3-5

GENERAL JOURNAL

Date	Account Titles and Explanation	PR	Debit	Credit
(a) Adjusting Entry:				
(b) Payday Entry:				

GENERAL JOURNAL

Date		Account Titles and Explanation	PR	Debit	Credit

Profit Margin Calculation:

(a) _____

(b) _____

(c) _____

(d) _____

(e) _____

Most Profitable: _____

Interpretation of Profit Margin: _____

_____

_____

GENERAL JOURNAL

Date	Account Titles and Explanation	PR	Debit	Credit
(a)				
(b)				

(c)

    Method in Part (a):

        Unearned Fees = $ _____

        Fees Earned   = $ _____

    Method in Part (b):

        Unearned Fees = $ _____

        Fees Earned   = $ _____

Chapter 3   Exercise 3-9^A *Name* _____

GENERAL JOURNAL

Date	Account Titles and Explanation	PR	Debit	Credit
(a)				
(b)				
(c)				
(d)				
(e)				
(f)				
(g)				

Balance Sheet

Income Statement

Statement of Retained Earnings

Balance Sheet

Current Ratio: _____

_____
_____
_____
_____
_____
_____

Interpretation: _____

_____
_____
_____
_____

Exercise 3-14

	Current Assets	Current Liabilities	Current Ratio
Case 1			
Case 2			
Case 3			
Case 4			
Case 5			

Analysis: _____

_____
_____
_____
_____

Part 1

GENERAL JOURNAL

Date	Account Titles and Explanation	PR	Debit	Credit

Part 2

GENERAL JOURNAL

Date	Account Titles and Explanation	PR	Debit	Credit

Part 3

GENERAL JOURNAL

Date	Account Titles and Explanation	PR	Debit	Credit

Name _____

GENERAL JOURNAL

Date		Account Titles and Explanation	PR	Debit	Credit

ACCOUNT TITLE	Unadjusted Trial Balance		Adjustments		Adjusted Trial Balance	
	Dr.	Cr.	Dr.	Cr.	Dr.	Cr.

_____ Company
Work Sheet

Part 1

GENERAL JOURNAL

Date	Account Titles and Explanation	PR	Debit	Credit

Part 1   (Continued)

GENERAL JOURNAL

Date		Account Titles and Explanation	PR	Debit	Credit

Part 2

GENERAL JOURNAL

Date		Account Titles and Explanation	PR	Debit	Credit

(1) _____   (7) _____
(2) _____   (8) _____
(3) _____   (9) _____
(4) _____   (10) _____
(5) _____   (11) _____
(6) _____   (12) _____

Part 1

ACCOUNT TITLES	UNADJUSTED TRIAL BALANCE		ADJUSTMENTS		ADJUSTED TRIAL BALANCE	
	DR	CR	DR	CR	DR	CR

Adjustment Descriptions

(a) _____

(b) _____

(c) _____

(d) _____

(e) _____

(f) _____

(g) _____

(h) _____

Part 2

_____

_____

Income Statement

_____

_____

_____

_____

_____

_____

_____

_____

_____

_____

_____

_____

_____

_____

_____

_____

_____

Statement of Retained Earnings

_____

_____

_____

_____

_____

_____

Balance Sheet

Part 1

Income Statement

Statement of Retained Earnings

Part 1   (Continued)

Balance Sheet

_____

_____

_____

_____

_____

_____

_____

_____

_____

_____

_____

_____

_____

_____

_____

_____

_____

_____

_____

_____

_____

_____

_____

_____

_____

Part 2

Profit Margin:

(1) ____	(6) ____	(11) ____	(16) ____
(2) ____	(7) ____	(12) ____	(17) ____
(3) ____	(8) ____	(13) ____	(18) ____
(4) ____	(9) ____	(14) ____	(19) ____
(5) ____	(10) ____	(15) ____	(20) ____

GENERAL LEDGER

Cash — ACCOUNT NO. 101

DATE	EXPLANATION	PR	DEBIT	CREDIT	BALANCE

Accounts Receivable — ACCOUNT NO. 106

DATE	EXPLANATION	PR	DEBIT	CREDIT	BALANCE

Office Supplies — ACCOUNT NO. 124

DATE	EXPLANATION	PR	DEBIT	CREDIT	BALANCE

Prepaid Insurance — ACCOUNT NO. 128

DATE	EXPLANATION	PR	DEBIT	CREDIT	BALANCE

Part 1   (Continued)

Computer Equipment*   ACCOUNT NO. 167

DATE	EXPLANATION	PR	DEBIT	CREDIT	BALANCE

Accumulated Depreciation-Computer Equipment*   ACCOUNT NO. 168

DATE	EXPLANATION	PR	DEBIT	CREDIT	BALANCE

Buildings**   ACCOUNT NO. 173

DATE	EXPLANATION	PR	DEBIT	CREDIT	BALANCE

Accumulated Depreciation-Buildings**   ACCOUNT NO. 174

DATE	EXPLANATION	PR	DEBIT	CREDIT	BALANCE

Salaries Payable   ACCOUNT NO. 209

DATE	EXPLANATION	PR	DEBIT	CREDIT	BALANCE

Common Stock   ACCOUNT NO. 307

DATE	EXPLANATION	PR	DEBIT	CREDIT	BALANCE

Retained Earnings   ACCOUNT NO. 318

DATE	EXPLANATION	PR	DEBIT	CREDIT	BALANCE

* Problem 3-7A only.
** Problem 3-7B only.

Dividends   ACCOUNT NO. 319

DATE	EXPLANATION	PR	DEBIT	CREDIT	BALANCE

Storage Fees Earned**   ACCOUNT NO. 401

DATE	EXPLANATION	PR	DEBIT	CREDIT	BALANCE

Commissions Earned*   ACCOUNT NO. 405

DATE	EXPLANATION	PR	DEBIT	CREDIT	BALANCE

Depreciation Expense—Buildings**   ACCOUNT NO. 606

DATE	EXPLANATION	PR	DEBIT	CREDIT	BALANCE

Depreciation Expense-Computer Equipment*   ACCOUNT NO. 612

DATE	EXPLANATION	PR	DEBIT	CREDIT	BALANCE

* Problem 3-7A only.

** Problem 3-7B only.

Part 1   (Continued)

Salaries Expense   ACCOUNT NO. 622

DATE	EXPLANATION	PR	DEBIT	CREDIT	BALANCE

Insurance Expense   ACCOUNT NO. 637

DATE	EXPLANATION	PR	DEBIT	CREDIT	BALANCE

Rent Expense   ACCOUNT NO. 640

DATE	EXPLANATION	PR	DEBIT	CREDIT	BALANCE

Office Supplies Expense   ACCOUNT NO. 650

DATE	EXPLANATION	PR	DEBIT	CREDIT	BALANCE

Repairs Expense   ACCOUNT NO. 684

DATE	EXPLANATION	PR	DEBIT	CREDIT	BALANCE

Telephone Expense   ACCOUNT NO. 688

DATE	EXPLANATION	PR	DEBIT	CREDIT	BALANCE

	Income Summary				ACCOUNT NO. 901
DATE	EXPLANATION	PR	DEBIT	CREDIT	BALANCE

GENERAL JOURNAL

Date	Account Titles and Explanation	PR	Debit	Credit

Part 3

Unadjusted Trial Balance		

Part 4   Adjusting Entries

GENERAL JOURNAL

Date		Account Titles and Explanation	PR	Debit	Credit

Income Statement

Statement of Retained Earnings

Balance Sheet

Part 6

Closing Entries:

GENERAL JOURNAL

Date	Account Titles and Explanation	PR	Debit	Credit

Part 7

Post-Closing Trial Balance

Part 1

_____

Income Statement

_____
_____
_____
_____
_____
_____
_____
_____
_____
_____
_____
_____
_____
_____
_____
_____
_____
_____
_____
_____
_____
_____
_____

Statement of Retained Earnings

Balance Sheet

Part 2

Closing Entries

GENERAL JOURNAL

Date	Account Titles and Explanation	PR	Debit	Credit

(1) _____

_____

_____

_____

(2) _____

_____

_____

_____

_____

_____

_____

_____

_____

_____

_____

_____

_____

_____

(3) 2010 Profit Margin: _____

_____

_____

   2009 Profit Margin: _____

_____

_____

(4) _____

_____

_____

_____

_____

(5) _____
_____
_____
_____
_____
_____
_____
_____
_____
_____

(6) _____
_____
_____
_____

(7) FastForward: _____
_____
_____
_____
_____
_____

Name _____

(1) Research In Motion

   Current Year Profit Margin:

   _____

   _____

   Prior Year Profit Margin:

   _____

   _____

   _____

   Apple

   Current Year Profit Margin:

   _____

   _____

   Prior Year Profit Margin:

   _____

   _____

   _____

(2) Analysis

   _____

   _____

   _____

(3) Research In Motion Current Ratio:

   Current Year

   _____

   Prior Year

   _____

   Apple Current Ratio:
   Current Year

   _____

   Prior Year

   _____

(4) _____

_____

_____

_____

_____

_____

(5) _____

_____

_____

_____

_____

_____

(6) _____

_____

_____

_____

_____

(1) _____
_____
_____
_____
_____
_____
_____
_____

(2) _____
_____
_____
_____
_____
_____
_____
_____
_____
_____
_____

(3) _____
_____
_____
_____
_____
_____

MEMORANDUM

TO:

FROM:

SUBJECT:

DATE:

(1) _____

_____

_____

(2) _____

_____

_____

(3) _____

_____

(4) _____

_____

(5) _____

_____

(6) _____

_____

_____

_____

(1) _____

GENERAL JOURNAL

Date	Account Titles and Explanation	PR	Debit	Credit
(a)				
(b)				

(2) _____

_____

_____

_____

_____

_____

_____

_____

(3) _____

_____

_____

_____

_____

_____

_____

Name _____

(1) _____

(2) _____

(3) _____

(4) _____

(5) _____

Global Decision—BTN 3-9

(1) _____

(2) Profit Margin

(3) Nokia Current Ratio:
    Current Year

    Prior Year

(4) _____

(1) _____   (6) _____
(2) _____   (7) _____
(3) _____   (8) _____
(4) _____   (9) _____
(5) _____   (10) _____

Quick Study 4-2

Answer: _____

GENERAL JOURNAL

Date		Account Titles and Explanation	PR	Debit	Credit

Quick Study 4-4

GENERAL JOURNAL

Date		Account Titles and Explanation	PR	Debit	Credit

Case (a)

_____
_____
_____
_____
_____
_____

Case (b)

_____
_____
_____
_____
_____
_____

Case (c)

_____
_____
_____
_____
_____
_____

Case (d)

_____
_____
_____
_____
_____
_____
_____

Interpretation of (a)

_____
_____
_____
_____

Quick Study 4-6

GENERAL JOURNAL

Date	Account Titles and Explanation	PR	Debit	Credit

GENERAL JOURNAL

Date		Account Titles and Explanation	PR	Debit	Credit

Quick Study 4-8:

Acid-Test Ratio: _____

_____

_____

_____

_____

Interpretation: _____

_____

_____

_____

_____
_____
_____
_____
_____
_____
_____
_____
_____
_____
_____

Quick Study 4-10

Answer: _____

Quick Study 4-11^A

(a) _____
(b) _____
(c) _____
(d) _____
(e) _____

GENERAL JOURNAL

Date	Account Titles and Explanation	PR	Debit	Credit

Quick Study 4-13^A

GENERAL JOURNAL

Date	Account Titles and Explanation	PR	Debit	Credit

Part 1

_____

Income Statement

_____
_____
_____
_____
_____
_____
_____
_____
_____
_____
_____

Part 2

_____

Income Statement

_____
_____
_____
_____
_____
_____
_____
_____
_____
_____
_____
_____

Quick Study 4-15

a. _____

b. _____

c. _____
_____

GENERAL JOURNAL

Date		Account Titles and Explanation	PR	Debit	Credit

(1) BUYER

GENERAL JOURNAL

Date		Account Titles and Explanation	PR	Debit	Credit

(2) SELLER

GENERAL JOURNAL

Date		Account Titles and Explanation	PR	Debit	Credit

(3)

_____
_____
_____
_____
_____
_____
_____
_____
_____
_____
_____
_____
_____

Exercise 4-3

_____ (a)
_____ (b)
_____ (c)
_____ (d)
_____ (e)

GENERAL JOURNAL

Date	Account Titles and Explanation	PR	Debit	Credit
Entries for Sale of Merchandise:				
Entries for (a):				
Entries for (b):				
Entries for (c):				

GENERAL JOURNAL

Date	Account Titles and Explanation	PR	Debit	Credit
Entries for Purchase of Merchandise:				
Entries for (a):				
Entries for (b):				
Entries for (c):				

(1) BUYER

GENERAL JOURNAL

Date		Account Titles and Explanation	PR	Debit	Credit

(2) SELLER

GENERAL JOURNAL

Date	Account Titles and Explanation	PR	Debit	Credit

Merchandise Inventory	

Cost of Goods Sold	

	(a)	(b)	(c)	(d)	(e)
Sales	$	$	$	$	$
Cost of goods sold					
Merchandise inventory (beg.)					
Total cost of merch. purchases					
Merchandise inventory (ending)					
Cost of goods sold					
Gross profit					
Expenses					
Net income (loss)	$	$	$	$	$

Work space:

Adjusting Entries:

GENERAL JOURNAL

Date	Account Titles and Explanation	PR	Debit	Credit

Closing Entries:

GENERAL JOURNAL

Date	Account Titles and Explanation	PR	Debit	Credit

_____
_____
_____
_____
_____
_____
_____
_____
_____
_____
_____
_____
_____
_____
_____
_____
_____
_____
_____
_____

Exercise 4-12

_____
_____
_____
_____
_____
_____

Name _____

	Case A	Case B	Case C
Current Ratio			

Acid-Test Ratio

Interpretation

PERPETUAL

GENERAL JOURNAL

Date	Account Titles and Explanation	PR	Debit	Credit

PERIODIC

GENERAL JOURNAL

Date	Account Titles and Explanation	PR	Debit	Credit

(1) BUYER

GENERAL JOURNAL

Date	Account Titles and Explanation	PR	Debit	Credit

(2) SELLER

GENERAL JOURNAL

Date	Account Titles and Explanation	PR	Debit	Credit

(1) BUYER

GENERAL JOURNAL

Date	Account Titles and Explanation	PR	Debit	Credit

(2) SELLER

GENERAL JOURNAL

Date	Account Titles and Explanation	PR	Debit	Credit

PERIODIC

GENERAL JOURNAL

Date		Account Titles and Explanation	PR	Debit	Credit

GENERAL JOURNAL

Date		Account Titles and Explanation	PR	Debit	Credit

GENERAL JOURNAL

Date		Account Titles and Explanation	PR	Debit	Credit

GENERAL JOURNAL

Date	Account Titles and Explanation	PR	Debit	Credit

Part 1

GENERAL JOURNAL

Date		Account Titles and Explanation	PR	Debit	Credit

Part 2

Income Statement

Part 3

Income Statement

Part 4

Income Statement

GENERAL JOURNAL

Date	Account Titles and Explanation	PR	Debit	Credit

Part 2

_____

_____

_____

_____

_____

_____

_____

_____

_____

_____

_____

_____

_____

_____

_____

_____

_____

Part 3

_____

_____

_____

_____

_____

_____

_____

_____

_____

_____

_____

_____

_____

Name _____

_____ Company

Work Sheet

Account Title	Unadjusted Trial Balance		Adjustments		Adjusted Trial Balance		Income Statement		Balance Sheet	
	Dr.	Cr.	Dr.	Cr.	Dr.	Cr.	Dr.	Cr.	Dr.	Cr.

Part 1

Part 2

Part 3
FastForward:

Part 1

_____
_____
_____
_____
_____
_____
_____
_____
_____
_____
_____
_____
_____
_____
_____
_____
_____
_____
_____
_____
_____

Part 2

_____
_____
_____
_____
_____
_____

Part 3

_____
_____
_____
_____
_____
_____
_____

Part 1

_____

_____

_____

_____

_____

_____

_____

_____

_____

_____

_____

_____

_____

_____

Part 2

_____

_____

_____

_____

_____

_____

_____

_____

MEMORANDUM

TO:
FROM:
DATE:
SUBJECT:

Fiscal Year ($ thousands)	2008	2009	2010
Net sales			
Cost of goods sold			
Gross margin			
Gross margin ratio			

Analysis:

_____

_____

_____

_____

_____

_____

_____

(1a)

_____
_____
_____
_____
_____
_____
_____

(1b)

_____
_____
_____
_____
_____
_____
_____
_____

(1c)

_____
_____
_____
_____
_____
_____
_____

(1d)

_____
_____
_____
_____
_____
_____

(1e)

_____
_____
_____
_____
_____
_____
_____
_____

(2)

Check: Net Income is _____.

_____
_____

(3)

_____
_____
_____
_____
_____
_____
_____
_____

Part 1

Forecasted Income Statement	
For Year Ended January 31, 2011	

_____

Part 2

_____

Part 3

_____

_____

_____

_____

_____

_____

_____

_____

_____

_____

_____

_____

_____

_____

_____

_____

_____

_____

_____

_____

_____

_____

_____

_____

(1) _____

_____

_____

_____

_____

_____

_____

_____

_____

_____

_____

_____

_____

_____

_____

_____

(2) _____

_____

_____

_____

_____

_____

_____

_____

Quick Study 5-1 (FIFO)   *Name* _____

Date	Purchases	Cost of Goods Sold	Inventory Balance

Quick Study 5-2 (LIFO)

Date	Purchases	Cost of Goods Sold	Inventory Balance

Quick Study 5-3 (WA)

Date	Purchases	Cost of Goods Sold	Inventory Balance

_____
_____
_____
_____
_____
_____
_____
_____
_____

Quick Study 5-5 (FIFO)

Date	Purchases	Cost of Goods Sold	Inventory Balance

Quick Study 5-6 (LIFO)

Date	Purchases	Cost of Goods Sold	Inventory Balance

Date	Purchases	Cost of Goods Sold	Inventory Balance

Quick Study 5-8 (Specific Identification)

Chapter 5   Quick Study 5-9   *Name* _____

(1) _____

(2) _____

(3) _____

(4) _____

(5) _____

Quick Study 5-10

_____
_____
_____
_____
_____
_____

Quick Study 5-11

_____
_____
_____
_____
_____
_____

Quick Study 5-12

Inventory Items	Units	Per Unit Cost	Market	Total Cost	Total Market	LCM applied to Items

LCM applied to products: _____

(a) _____

(b) _____

(c) _____

(d) _____

(e) _____

(f) _____

Quick Study 5-14

Inventory Turnover

_____

_____

Days' Sales in Inventory

_____

_____

_____

Quick Study 5-15[A]

_____

_____

_____

_____

Quick Study 5-16[A]

_____

_____

_____

_____

Quick Study 5-17[A]

_____

_____

_____

_____
_____
_____

Quick Study 5-19[A]

_____
_____
_____

Quick Study 5-20[A]

_____
_____
_____

Quick Study 5-21[A]

_____
_____
_____

Quick Study 5-22[B]

_____
_____
_____
_____
_____

Quick Study 5-23

a. _____
_____
_____

b. _____
_____
_____

c. _____
_____
_____

Chapter 5   Exercise 5-1   Name _MICHAEL HARJU_

(1)

_____

_____

(2)

_____

_____

_____

Exercise 5-2

_____

_____

_____

_____

_____

_____

_____

Exercise 5-3

(a) Specific Identification

MAR. 30 COST OF GOODS

       ENDING INVENTORY

_____

_____

_____

_____

_____

(b) Weighted Average Perpetual

Date	Purchases	Cost of Goods Sold	Inventory Balance

(c) FIFO Perpetual

Date	Purchases	Cost of Goods Sold	Inventory Balance

(d) LIFO Perpetual

Date	Purchases	Cost of Goods Sold	Inventory Balance

_____ COMPANY Income Statements For Month Ended January 31				
	Specific Identification	Weighted Average	FIFO	LIFO

(1) _____

_____

(2) _____

_____

(3) _____

_____

(a) FIFO Perpetual

Date	Purchases	Cost of Goods Sold	Inventory Balance

FIFO Gross Margin:

(b) LIFO Perpetual

Date	Purchases	Cost of Goods Sold	Inventory Balance

LIFO Gross Margin:

Name _____

Specific Identification Method

(a) Ending Inventory and Cost of Goods Sold: _____

_____

_____

_____

_____

_____

_____

_____

_____

_____

_____

_____

_____

(b) Gross Margin: _____

_____

_____

_____

_____

_____

_____

Inventory Items	Units	Per Unit		Total Cost	Total Market	LCM applied to Products
		Cost	Market			

LCM applied to products: _____

Exercise 5-8

(1) Gross Profit _____

_____

_____

(2)

	2010	2011	2012
Sales			
Cost of goods sold			
Beginning inventory			
Cost of Purchases			
Goods avail. for sale			
Ending Inventory			
Cost of goods sold			
Gross Profit			

(1) (a) _____

_____

_____

_____

_____

_____

(b) _____

_____

_____

_____

_____

_____

_____

(2) _____

_____

_____

_____

_____

_____

_____

Inventory Turnover (2010):

_____
_____
_____

Inventory Turnover (2011):

_____
_____
_____

Days' Sales in Inventory (2010):

_____
_____
_____

Days' Sales in Inventory (2011):

_____
_____
_____

Analysis Comments:

_____
_____
_____
_____

Chapter 5   Exercise 5-11[A]   *Name* _____

Method and Computations	Ending Inventory	Cost of Goods Sold
(a) Specific Identification		
(b) Weighted Average Periodic		
(c) FIFO Periodic		
(d) LIFO Periodic		

Method and Computations	Ending Inventory	Cost of Goods Sold
(a) FIFO Periodic		
(b) LIFO Periodic		
(c) FIFO Gross Margin		
LIFO Gross Margin		

Method and Computations	Ending Inventory	Cost of Goods Sold
(a) Specific Identification		
(b) Weighted Average Periodic		
(c) FIFO Periodic		
(d) LIFO Periodic		
Income Effect(s):		

Method and Computations	Ending Inventory	Cost of Goods Sold
(a) Specific Identification		
(b) Weighted Average Periodic		
(c) FIFO Periodic		
(d) LIFO Periodic		

Income Effect(s):

	At Cost	At Retail

Exercise 5-16^B

Exercise 5-17

a.

b.

c.

(1) Cost of Goods Available for Sale and Units Available for Sale:

_____

_____
_____
_____
_____
_____
_____
_____
_____
_____
_____
_____

(2) Ending Inventory (in Units):

_____
_____
_____
_____

(3a) FIFO Perpetual

Date	Purchases	Cost of Goods Sold	Inventory Balance

(3b) LIFO Perpetual

Date	Purchases	Cost of Goods Sold	Inventory Balance

(3c) Weighted Average Perpetual

Date	Purchases	Cost of Goods Sold	Inventory Balance

(3d) Specific Identification

_____
_____
_____
_____
_____
_____
_____
_____
_____
_____
_____
_____
_____
_____
_____
_____
_____

(4) Gross Profit

	FIFO	LIFO	Weighted Average	Specific Identification
Sales				
Less cost of goods sold				
Gross profit				

(1) Cost of Goods Available for Sale and Units Available for Sale:

_____
_____
_____
_____
_____
_____
_____
_____
_____
_____
_____

(2) Ending Inventory (in Units):

_____
_____
_____
_____

(3a) FIFO Perpetual

Date	Purchases	Cost of Goods Sold	Inventory Balance

(3b) LIFO Perpetual

Date	Purchases	Cost of Goods Sold	Inventory Balance

(3c) Specific Identification

(3d) Weighted Average Perpetual

Date	Purchases	Cost of Goods Sold	Inventory Balance

(4) Gross Profit

	FIFO	LIFO	Specific Identification	Weighted Average
Sales				
Less cost of goods sold				
Gross profit				

(5) _____

_____

_____

_____

_____

_____

_____

Inventory Items	Units	Per Unit		Total Cost	Total Market	LCM applied to Items
		Cost	Market			

(1) _____

(2)

GENERAL JOURNAL

Date	Account Titles and Explanation	PR	Debit	Credit

Part 1

(a) Cost of Goods Sold	2010	2011	2012
Reported.............................			
Adjustments: 12/31/2010 error			
12/31/2011 error			
Corrected..............................			

(b) Net Income	2010	2011	2012
Reported.............................			
Adjustments: 12/31/2010 error			
12/31/2011 error			
Corrected..............................			

(c) Total Current Assets	2010	2011	2012
Reported.............................			
Adjustments: 12/31/2010 error			
12/31/2011 error			
Corrected..............................			

(d) Equity	2010	2011	2012
Reported.............................			
Adjustments: 12/31/2010 error			
12/31/2011 error			
Corrected..............................			

Part 2

_____
_____
_____
_____
_____
_____

Part 3

_____
_____
_____
_____
_____

Part 1

Units Available for Sale and Cost of Units Available for Sale:

_____
_____
_____
_____
_____
_____
_____
_____

Part 2

(a) FIFO Periodic

_____
_____
_____
_____
_____
_____
_____
_____
_____

(b) LIFO Periodic

_____
_____
_____
_____
_____
_____
_____
_____

(c) Weighted Average Periodic

_____
_____
_____
_____
_____
_____
_____

Part 1

Comparative Income Statements

	FIFO	LIFO	Weighted Average
Income Statements Comparing FIFO, LIFO and Weighted Average **For Year Ended December 31, 2011**			

Supporting Calculations:

Part 2

_____
_____
_____
_____
_____
_____
_____

Part 3

Advantages:
   LIFO
_____
_____
   FIFO
_____
_____

Disadvantages:
   LIFO
_____
_____
   FIFO
_____
_____

Part 1

_____ Company Estimated Inventory December 31	At Cost	At Retail

Part 2

_____ Company Inventory Shortage December 31	At Cost	At Retail

_____ Company
Estimated Inventory
March 31

Part A

1.

Inventory Items	Units	Per Unit Cost	Per Unit Market	Total Cost	Total Market	LCM applied to Whole

_____
_____
_____
_____

2.

Inventory Items	Units	Per Unit Cost	Per Unit Market	Total Cost	Total Market	LCM applied to Items

_____
_____
_____
_____

Part B

(1) Inventory Turnover: _____
_____
_____

   Days' Sales in Inventory: _____
_____
_____

(2) Analysis: _____
_____
_____
_____
_____

(1) _____

_____

_____

(2) 2010: _____

_____

_____

2009: _____

_____

_____

_____

(3) _____

_____

_____

_____

_____

(4) _____

_____

_____

_____

_____

(5a) Inventory Turnover:

_____

_____

_____

_____

(5b) Days' Sales in Inventory:

_____

_____

_____

_____

_____

(6)   FastForward:

_____

_____

_____

_____

_____

_____

_____

_____

_____

_____

_____

_____

_____

_____

_____

(1)
Inventory Turnover—Research In Motion:

_____
_____
_____
_____

Inventory Turnover—Apple:

_____
_____
_____
_____
_____

(2)
Days' Sales in Inventory—Research In Motion:

_____
_____
_____
_____
_____
_____
_____

Days' Sales in Inventory—Apple:

_____
_____
_____
_____
_____
_____
_____

Chapter 5   Comparative Analysis   Name _____
                    BTN 5-2
                    (Continued)

(3) Interpretation: _____

_____

_____

_____

_____

_____

_____

_____

Ethics Challenge—BTN 5-3

(1) **Profit Margin:** _____

_____

_____

_____

_____

    Current Ratio: _____

_____

_____

_____

_____

(2) _____

_____

_____

_____

_____

_____

_____

_____

_____

_____

MEMORANDUM

TO:

FROM:

SUBJECT:

DATE:

(1) _____
_____
_____

(2) _____
_____

(3) **Gross Margin:** _____
_____

Gross Margin Ratio: _____
_____

(4) _____

Inventory Turnover: _____
_____
_____

Days' Sales in Inventory _____
_____
_____
_____

Teamwork in Action—BTN 5-6

(a) and (b) Concept discussion: _____
_____
_____
_____
_____
_____
_____
_____
_____

(a) and (b) Procedures:

Date	Purchases	Cost of Goods Sold	Inventory Balance

(c)

(d)

(e)

(1)(a) Inventory Turnover

_____

_____

_____

Day's Sales in Inventory

_____

_____

_____

(b) Inventory Turnover

_____

_____

_____

Day's Sales in Inventory

_____

_____

_____

(2) _____

_____

_____

_____

_____

_____

_____

_____

_____
_____
_____
_____
_____
_____
_____
_____
_____
_____
_____
_____
_____
_____
_____
_____
_____

Global Decision—BTN 5-9

(1) Inventory Turnover: _____
_____
_____
_____
_____
_____
_____

Days' Sales in Inventory: _____
_____
_____
_____
_____
_____
_____
_____

(2) Interpretation: _____
_____
_____
_____
_____

(1) _____

_____

_____

_____

(2) _____

_____

_____

_____

(3) _____

_____

_____

_____

Quick Study 6-2

(1) (a) _____

(b) _____

(c) _____

(2) (a) _____

(b) _____

Quick Study 6-3

(1) _____

_____

_____

(2) _____

_____

(3) _____

_____

_____

(1)

GENERAL JOURNAL

Date	Account Titles and Explanation	PR	Debit	Credit
(a) Establishment of the Fund:				
(b) Reimbursement of the Fund:				

(2) _____

_____

_____

_____

Parts 1 and 2

	(1)		(2)
	Bank or Book Effect	**Add or Subtract**	**Adjusting Entry Required or Not**
(a)			
(b)			
(c)			
(d)			
(e)			
(f)			
(g)			

Quick Study 6-6

Bank Reconciliation

Name _____

Days' Sales Uncollected (2011):

_____
_____
_____
_____

Days' Sales Uncollected (2010):

_____
_____
_____
_____

Interpretation and Explanation:

_____
_____
_____
_____

Quick Study 6-8[A]

_____
_____
_____
_____
_____
_____

Quick Study 6-9[B]

(a) _____

(b) _____
_____
_____

a. _____

_____

_____

_____

b. _____

_____

_____

_____

_____

Quick Study 6-11

a. _____

_____

_____

_____

b. (1) _____

_____

_____

_____

_____

_____

(2) _____

_____

_____

_____

_____

(1) _____
_____
_____
_____
_____

(2) _____
_____
_____
_____
_____
_____
_____

Exercise 6-2
Evaluation: _____
_____
_____

Principles Ignored: _____
_____
_____
_____
_____

Exercise 6-3
(a) Internal Control Problems: _____
_____
_____
_____
_____
_____
_____

(b) Internal Control Recommendations: _____
_____
_____
_____
_____

(1) _____

_____

_____

_____

_____

(2) _____

_____

_____

_____

(3) _____

_____

_____

_____

_____

_____

(1) Establish the Fund

GENERAL JOURNAL

Date		Account Titles and Explanation	PR	Debit	Credit

(2) Reimburse the Fund

GENERAL JOURNAL

Date		Account Titles and Explanation	PR	Debit	Credit

(3) Adjust the Fund Balance

GENERAL JOURNAL

Date		Account Titles and Explanation	PR	Debit	Credit

(1) Establish the Fund

GENERAL JOURNAL

Date		Account Titles and Explanation	PR	Debit	Credit

(2) Reimburse the Fund

GENERAL JOURNAL

Date		Account Titles and Explanation	PR	Debit	Credit

(3) Reimburse and Increase the Fund

GENERAL JOURNAL

Date		Account Titles and Explanation	PR	Debit	Credit

	Bank Balance		Book Balance			Not Shown on
	Add	Deduct	Add	Deduct	Adjust	Reconciliation
1. Bank service charge.						
2. Checks written and mailed to payees on October 2.						
3. Check written by another depositor but charged against this company's account.						
4. Principal and interest on a note receivable to this company is collected by the bank but not yet recorded by the company.						
5. Special bank charge for collection of note in No. 4 on company's behalf.						
6. Check written against the company account and cleared by the bank; erroneously not recorded by the company recordkeeper.						
7. Interest earned on the account.						
8. Deposit made on September 30 after the bank closed.						
9. Checks outstanding on August 31 that cleared the bank in September.						
10. NSF check from customer returned on Sept. 25 but not recorded by this company.						
11. Checks written by the company and mailed to payees on September 30.						
12. Deposit made on September 5 and processed by bank on September 6.						

Chapter 6   Exercise 6-8   *Name* _____

(1) _____

_____

_____

(2) _____

_____

(3) _____

_____

Exercise 6-9

_____

Bank Reconciliation

_____

_____

_____

_____

_____

_____

_____

_____

Exercise 6-10

GENERAL JOURNAL

Date	Account Titles and Explanation	PR	Debit	Credit

Bank Reconciliation

_____

_____

_____

_____

_____

_____

_____

_____

_____

_____

_____

_____

_____

Exercise 6-12

(a)

Days' Sales Uncollected (2010):

_____

_____

_____

Days' Sales Uncollected (2011):

_____

_____

_____

_____

(b) Interpretation of Change:

_____

_____

_____

_____

Exercise 6-13[A]

(1)	(3)	(5)
(2)	(4)	(6)

(a) Recording Invoices at Gross Amounts—Gross Method

GENERAL JOURNAL

Date	Account Titles and Explanation	PR	Debit	Credit

(b) Recording Invoices at Net Amounts—Net Method

GENERAL JOURNAL

Date	Account Titles and Explanation	PR	Debit	Credit

(1) Principle Violated:

    Recommended

(2) Principle Violated:

    Recommended

(3) Principle Violated:

    Recommended

(4) Principle Violated:

    Recommended

(5) Principle Violated:

    Recommended

Part 1

GENERAL JOURNAL

Date	Account Titles and Explanation	PR	Debit	Credit

Part 2

_____

_____

_____

_____

_____

_____

_____

_____

_____

_____

Part 1

GENERAL JOURNAL

Date		Account Titles and Explanation	PR	Debit	Credit

Part 2

_____

_____

Petty Cash Payments Report

_____

_____

_____

_____

_____

_____

_____

_____

_____

_____

_____

_____

_____

_____

_____

_____

Part 3

GENERAL JOURNAL

Date		Account Titles and Explanation	PR	Debit	Credit

Part 1

Bank Reconciliation

Part 2

GENERAL JOURNAL

Date	Account Titles and Explanation	PR	Debit	Credit

Part 3

(a) _____

_____

_____

_____

_____

_____

(b) _____

_____

_____

_____

_____

_____

_____

Problem 6-5A or 6-5B
Part 1

_____

_____

Bank Reconciliation

Chapter 6   Problem 6-5A or 6-5B   Name _____
             (Continued)

Part 2

GENERAL JOURNAL

Date	Account Titles and Explanation	PR	Debit	Credit

Part 3

(1) _____

_____

(2) _____

_____

(3) _____

_____

Bank Reconciliation

Part 2

GENERAL JOURNAL

Date	Account Titles and Explanation	PR	Debit	Credit

Chapter 6 Reporting in Action—BTN 6-1 *Name* _____

Part 1

Account	Fiscal Year 2010		Fiscal Year 2009	
	Balance ($)	Cash & Equiv. as % of Bal.	Balance ($)	Cash & Equiv. as % of Bal.

Interpretation: _____

_____

_____

Part 2

_____

_____

_____

_____

_____

_____

_____

_____

_____

Part 3

Days' Sales Uncollected (2010):

_____
_____
_____
_____
_____

Days' Sales Uncollected (2009):

_____
_____
_____
_____
_____

Interpretation:

_____
_____
_____
_____
_____

Part 4

FastForward:

_____
_____
_____
_____
_____
_____
_____
_____
_____

Research In Motion:
Days' Sales Uncollected (Current year): _____
_____
_____

Days' Sales Uncollected (Prior year): _____
_____
_____

Interpretation: _____
_____
_____
_____

Apple:
Days' Sales Uncollected (Current year): _____
_____
_____

Days' Sales Uncollected (Prior year): _____
_____
_____

Interpretation: _____
_____
_____
_____

Comparison - Research In Motion vs. Apple _____
_____
_____
_____
_____

(1) _____

_____

_____

_____

_____

(2) _____

_____

_____

_____

_____

(3) _____

_____

_____

_____

_____

_____

_____

_____

(4) _____

_____

_____

_____

_____

_____

_____

_____

MEMORANDUM

TO:

FROM:

SUBJECT:

DATE:

(1) _____

_____

_____

(2) _____

_____

_____

(3) _____

_____

_____

(4) _____

_____

_____

(5) _____

_____

_____

(6) _____

_____

_____

(7) _____

_____

_____

(8) _____

_____

_____

(9) _____

_____

_____

(1) _____

_____

(2) _____

_____

(3) _____

_____

(4) _____

_____

(5) _____

_____

(6) _____

_____

(7) _____

_____

(8) _____

_____

(9) _____

_____

(10) _____

_____

(1) (a) _____

_____

_____

    (b) _____

_____

_____

    (c) _____

_____

_____

    (d) _____

_____

_____

    (e) _____

_____

_____

    (f) _____

_____

_____

    (g) _____

_____

_____

(2) _____

_____

_____

Hitting the Road—BTN 6-8

_____

_____

_____

_____

_____

_____

1.

Accounts	Current Year Balance	Cash as % of Bal.	Prior Year Balance	Cash as % of Bal.
Cash...........................				
Current assets..........				
Total assets...............				
Current liabilities.......				
Stockholders' equity...				

Analysis Comment:

_____

_____

_____

2.

_____

_____

_____

_____

_____

_____

3.

Days' Sales Uncollected

Current Year:

_____

_____

_____

Prior Year:

_____

_____

_____

Assessment:

_____

_____

_____

_____

(1)

GENERAL JOURNAL

Date		Account Titles and Explanation	PR	Debit	Credit

(2)

GENERAL JOURNAL

Date		Account Titles and Explanation	PR	Debit	Credit

a. _____

_____

_____

_____

_____

b. _____

_____

_____

_____

_____

GENERAL JOURNAL

Date		Account Titles and Explanation	PR	Debit	Credit

Part 1

GENERAL LEDGER

Accounts Receivable	Sales	Sales Returns and Allowances

ACCOUNTS RECEIVABLE LEDGER

Surf Shop	Yum Enterprises	Matt Albin

Part 2

_____
_____
Schedule of Accounts Receivable
_____
_____
_____
_____
_____

Comparison:
_____
_____
_____

GENERAL JOURNAL

Date		Account Titles and Explanation	PR	Debit	Credit

Exercise 7-4

GENERAL JOURNAL

Date		Account Titles and Explanation	PR	Debit	Credit

(a)

GENERAL JOURNAL

Date	Account Titles and Explanation	PR	Debit	Credit

(b)

GENERAL JOURNAL

Date	Account Titles and Explanation	PR	Debit	Credit

(a) _____

_____

_____

_____

_____

_____

(b)

GENERAL JOURNAL

Date		Account Titles and Explanation	PR	Debit	Credit

(c)

GENERAL JOURNAL

Date		Account Titles and Explanation	PR	Debit	Credit

Exercise 7-7

(a) _____

_____

_____

_____

_____

(b)

GENERAL JOURNAL

Date	Account Titles and Explanation	PR	Debit	Credit

(c)

GENERAL JOURNAL

Date	Account Titles and Explanation	PR	Debit	Credit

Exercise 7-8

GENERAL JOURNAL

Date	Account Titles and Explanation	PR	Debit	Credit

(a)

GENERAL JOURNAL

Date	Account Titles and Explanation	PR	Debit	Credit

(b)

GENERAL JOURNAL

Date	Account Titles and Explanation	PR	Debit	Credit

(c)

GENERAL JOURNAL

Date	Account Titles and Explanation	PR	Debit	Credit

GENERAL JOURNAL

Date	Account Titles and Explanation	PR	Debit	Credit

Financial Statement Note(s): _____

_____

_____

_____

GENERAL JOURNAL

Date		Account Titles and Explanation	PR	Debit	Credit

Exercise 7-12

GENERAL JOURNAL

Date		Account Titles and Explanation	PR	Debit	Credit

GENERAL JOURNAL

Date	Account Titles and Explanation	PR	Debit	Credit

2010

GENERAL JOURNAL

Date	Account Titles and Explanation	PR	Debit	Credit

Supporting work:

2011

GENERAL JOURNAL

Date	Account Titles and Explanation	PR	Debit	Credit

Supporting work:

Part 1

GENERAL JOURNAL

Date	Account Titles and Explanation	PR	Debit	Credit
(a)				
(b)				
(c)				

Part 2

_____

_____

_____

_____

_____

_____

_____

_____

Part 3

_____
_____
_____
_____
_____
_____
_____

Problem 7-4A or 7-4B

Part 1

_____
_____
_____
_____
_____
_____
_____

Part 2

GENERAL JOURNAL

Date	Account Titles and Explanation	PR	Debit	Credit

Part 3

_____
_____
_____
_____
_____
_____
_____
_____

Part 1

Date		Account Titles and Explanation	PR	Debit	Credit
2010					
2011					

(1) _____

_____

(2) Accounts Receivable Turnover (2010):

_____

_____

(3) Average Collection Period:

_____

_____

  Analysis:

_____

_____

(4) Liquid Assets as a percent of Current Liabilities (2010):

_____

_____

  Liquid Assets as a percent of Current Liabilities (2009):

_____

_____

  Comparison and Interpretation:

_____

_____

_____

(5) _____

_____

_____

_____

(6) FastForward:

_____

_____

_____

_____

(1) RIM's Accounts Receivable Turnover (Current Year and Prior Year):

_____
_____
_____
_____

   Apple's Accounts Receivable Turnover (Current Year and Prior Year):

_____
_____
_____
_____
_____

(2) RIM's Average Collection Period (Current Year and Prior Year):

_____
_____
_____

   Apple's Average Collection Period (Current Year and Prior Year):

_____
_____
_____
_____
_____
_____

   Interpretation:

_____
_____

(3) Efficiency Comparison:

_____
_____
_____
_____
_____

(1) _____
_____
_____
_____
_____
_____
_____

(2) _____
_____
_____
_____
_____
_____
_____
_____
_____

(3) _____
_____
_____
_____
_____
_____
_____

MEMORANDUM

TO:

FROM:

SUBJECT:

DATE:

(1) _____
_____
_____
_____
_____
_____
_____

(2) _____ **Dec. 31, 2009**   **Dec. 31, 2008**
_____
_____
_____
_____
_____

(3) _____
_____
_____
_____
_____

Estimate of Uncollectibles: _____

_____

_____

_____

_____

_____

_____

_____

Adjusting Entry:

GENERAL JOURNAL

Date	Account Titles and Explanation	PR	Debit	Credit

Presentation of Net Realizable Accounts Receivable in Balance Sheet:

_____

_____

_____

_____

_____

Part 1

Added Monthly Net Income (Loss) under Plan A

Added Monthly Net Income (Loss) under Plan B

Part 2

_____
_____
_____
_____
_____
_____
_____
_____
_____
_____
_____
_____
_____

Global Decision—BTN 7-9

(1) Accounts Receivable Turnover

_____
_____
_____
_____

(2) Average Collection Period

_____
_____
_____

(3) Analysis

_____
_____
_____

(4) Percent of Receivables per Category

_____
_____
_____
_____

_____
_____
_____
_____
_____
_____

Quick Study 8-2

(1) _____
_____
_____

(2) _____
_____
_____

(3) _____
_____
_____

Quick Study 8-3

Straight-line: _____
_____

Quick Study 8-4

Units-of-Production: _____
_____
_____
_____

Quick Study 8-5

Revised Straight-Line Depreciation: _____
_____
_____
_____
_____

First Year: _____

_____

Second Year: _____

_____

Third Year: _____

_____

Quick Study 8-7

GENERAL JOURNAL

Date		Account Titles and Explanation	PR	Debit	Credit
(a)					

Quick Study 8-8

(1)

   (a) _____

   (b) _____

   (c) _____

   (d) _____

(2)

GENERAL JOURNAL

Date		Account Titles and Explanation	PR	Debit	Credit
(a)					
(d)					

GENERAL JOURNAL

Date	Account Titles and Explanation	PR	Debit	Credit
(1)				
(2)				
(3)				

Quick Study 8-10

GENERAL JOURNAL

Date	Account Titles and Explanation	PR	Debit	Credit
(1)				
(2)				

Intangible Asset(s): _____

_____

_____

Natural Resource(s): _____

_____

_____

Quick Study 8-12

GENERAL JOURNAL

Date	Account Titles and Explanation	PR	Debit	Credit
(1)				
(2)				

Quick Study 8-13

Total Asset Turnover: _____

_____

_____

_____

Interpretation: _____

_____

_____

_____

GENERAL JOURNAL

Date	Account Titles and Explanation	PR	Debit	Credit
(1)				
(2)				

Quick Study 8-15

a. _____

_____

_____

b. _____

_____

_____

Exercise 8-1

Total Cost to be Recorded: _____

_____

_____

_____

_____

_____

_____

Cost of Land:

_____
_____
_____

Cost of New Bldg & Land Improv:

_____
_____
_____
_____

GENERAL JOURNAL

Date	Account Titles and Explanation	PR	Debit	Credit

Exercise 8-3

Allocation of Costs to Assets:

_____
_____
_____
_____
_____
_____
_____
_____

GENERAL JOURNAL

Date	Account Titles and Explanation	PR	Debit	Credit

Straight-Line Depreciation:

Year	Annual Depreciation	Year-End Book Value

Exercise 8-5

Double-Declining-Balance Depreciation:

Year	Beginning-Year Book Value	Depreciation Rate	Annual Depreciation	Year-End Book Value

Straight-Line

_____

_____

_____

_____

Exercise 8-7

Units-of-Production:

_____

_____

_____

Exercise 8-8

Double-Declining-Balance:

_____

_____

_____

_____

Exercise 8-9

Straight-Line:

_____

_____

_____

Exercise 8-10

Double-Declining-Balance:

_____

_____

_____

_____

Name _____

(1) _____

_____

_____

_____

_____

_____

(2) _____

_____

_____

_____

_____

_____

_____

Exercise 8-12

Straight-Line Depreciation:

Year	Income before Depreciation	Depreciation Expense	Net Income

Exercise 8-13

Double-Declining-Balance Depreciation:

Year	Income before Depreciation	Depreciation Expense	Net Income

(1) _____

_____

_____

_____

_____

(2)

GENERAL JOURNAL

Date		Account Titles and Explanation	PR	Debit	Credit

(3) _____

_____

_____

_____

_____

(4)

GENERAL JOURNAL

Date		Account Titles and Explanation	PR	Debit	Credit

GENERAL JOURNAL

Date	Account Titles and Explanation	PR	Debit	Credit
(1)				
(2)				
(3)				

Exercise 8-16

GENERAL JOURNAL

Date	Account Titles and Explanation	PR	Debit	Credit
(1)				
(2)				
(3)				
(4)				

GENERAL JOURNAL

Date	Account Titles and Explanation	PR	Debit	Credit
Record depreciation:				
(1)				
(2)				

Computations:

Exercise 8-18

GENERAL JOURNAL

Date	Account Titles and Explanation	PR	Debit	Credit

GENERAL JOURNAL

Date		Account Titles and Explanation	PR	Debit	Credit

Exercise 8-20

(1) Value of Goodwill: _____

_____

_____

_____

(2) _____

_____

_____

(3) _____

_____

_____

Exercise 8-21

(1) _____

_____

(2) _____

_____

(3) _____

_____

Total Asset Turnover (2010):

_____

_____

_____

Total Asset Turnover (2011):

_____

_____

_____

Efficiency Analysis:

_____

_____

_____

_____

Exercise 8-23[A]

(1) _____

_____

_____

_____

(2) _____

_____

_____

_____

(3) _____

_____

_____

_____

GENERAL JOURNAL

Date	Account Titles and Explanation	PR	Debit	Credit
(1)				
(2)				
(3)				

Exercise 8-25

GENERAL JOURNAL

Date	Account Titles and Explanation	PR	Debit	Credit
(1)				
(2)				
(3)				
(4)				

Part 1

	Estimated Market Value	Percent of Total	Apportioned Cost
Building..			
Land..			
Land Improvements...........................			
Vehicles (or Trucks).........................			
Total..			

GENERAL JOURNAL

Date	Account Titles and Explanation	PR	Debit	Credit

Part 2

_____
_____
_____
_____

Part 3

_____
_____
_____
_____
_____

Part 4

_____
_____
_____
_____
_____

Part 1

	Land	Building 2 (or B)	Building 3 (or C)	Land Improv. 1 (or B)	Land Improv. 2 (or C)
Purchase price..........					
Demolition...............					
Land grading.............					
New building............					
New improvements....					
Totals.....................					

Computations:

Part 2

GENERAL JOURNAL

Date	Account Titles and Explanation	PR	Debit	Credit

Part 3

GENERAL JOURNAL

Date	Account Titles and Explanation	PR	Debit	Credit

2010:

GENERAL JOURNAL

Date	Account Titles and Explanation	PR	Debit	Credit

Supporting work:

2011:

GENERAL JOURNAL

Date	Account Titles and Explanation	PR	Debit	Credit

Supporting work:

2010:

GENERAL JOURNAL

Date	Account Titles and Explanation	PR	Debit	Credit

2011:

GENERAL JOURNAL

Date	Account Titles and Explanation	PR	Debit	Credit

Supporting work:

2012:

GENERAL JOURNAL

Date		Account Titles and Explanation	PR	Debit	Credit

Supporting work:

Year	Straight-Line	Units-of-Production	Double-Declining-Balance
1			
2			
3			
4			
5 (for 8-5B)	_____	_____	_____
Totals	=========	=========	=========

Workspace: _____

Straight-Line: _____

_____
_____

Units-of-Production: _____

_____
_____
_____
_____

Double-Declining-Balance: _____

_____
_____
_____
_____

Problem 8-6A or 8-6B

Part 1

GENERAL JOURNAL

Date	Account Titles and Explanation	PR	Debit	Credit

Part 2
(a) and (b)

GENERAL JOURNAL

Date		Account Titles and Explanation	PR	Debit	Credit

Part 3

GENERAL JOURNAL

Date		Account Titles and Explanation	PR	Debit	Credit
(a) Sold for $ _____ cash:					
(b) Sold for $ _____ cash:					
(c) Destroyed in fire, collected $_____ cash from insurance.					

GENERAL JOURNAL

Date	Account Titles and Explanation	PR	Debit	Credit
(a)				
(b)				
(c)				
(d)				

Analysis Component:

_____

_____

_____

_____

_____

_____

_____

(1) As of February 27, 2010: _____

_____

_____

_____

   As of February 28, 2009: _____

_____

_____

_____

(2) _____

_____

_____

_____

(3) _____

_____

_____

_____

_____

_____

_____

(4) Total Asset Turnover (2010): _____

_____

_____

_____

   Total Asset Turnover (2009): _____

_____

_____

_____

(5) FastForward: _____

_____

_____

_____

_____

_____

(1) Total Asset Turnover (RIM):
_____
        Current Year
_____

_____

_____
        One Year Prior
_____

_____

    Total Asset Turnover (Apple):
_____
        Current Year
_____

_____

        One Year Prior
_____

_____

_____

(2) Efficiency Analysis:
_____

_____

_____

_____

_____

_____

(1) _____

_____

_____

_____

_____

_____

(2) _____

_____

_____

_____

_____

_____

_____

_____

_____

_____

(3) _____

_____

_____

_____

_____

_____

_____

_____

DATA FOR MEMORANDUM						
Total Asset Turnover	Company 1	Company 2	Company 3	Company 4	Company 5	Average

MEMORANDUM

TO:
FROM:
SUBJECT:
DATE:

(1)

_____
_____
_____
_____
_____

(2)

	Amount	Dollar Change from Prior Year	Percent Change

(3)

_____
_____
_____
_____
_____

(4)

_____
_____
_____
_____

Presentation Outline

Method of Expertise: _____
_____
_____
_____
_____

Depreciation Expense: _____
_____
_____
_____
_____
_____

Explanations: _____
_____
_____
_____
_____
_____

Analysis Versus Other Methods: _____
_____
_____
_____
_____

Book Value and Reporting: _____
_____
_____
_____
_____

Name _____

Part 1

(a) _____
_____
_____
_____
_____
_____
_____
_____
_____

(b) _____
_____
_____
_____
_____
_____
_____

Part 2
_____
_____
_____
_____
_____
_____

_____
_____
_____
_____
_____
_____
_____
_____
_____
_____
_____
_____
_____
_____
_____
_____
_____
_____
_____

Global Decision—BTN 8-9

(1) Total Asset Turnover (Current Year): _____
_____
_____

   Total Asset Turnover (Prior Year): _____
_____
_____
_____

(2) _____
_____
_____
_____
_____
_____
_____

Current Liabilities: _____

_____

_____

Quick Study 9-2

GENERAL JOURNAL

Date	Account Titles and Explanation	PR	Debit	Credit

Quick Study 9-3

GENERAL JOURNAL

Date	Account Titles and Explanation	PR	Debit	Credit

(1) _____

_____

(2) _____

_____

(3) _____

_____

Quick Study 9-5

(1) Accrued Interest Payable: _____

_____

_____

_____

(2) & (3)

GENERAL JOURNAL

Date		Account Titles and Explanation	PR	Debit	Credit

Quick Study 9-6

GENERAL JOURNAL

Date		Account Titles and Explanation	PR	Debit	Credit

GENERAL JOURNAL

Date	Account Titles and Explanation	PR	Debit	Credit

Quick Study 9-8

GENERAL JOURNAL

Date	Account Titles and Explanation	PR	Debit	Credit

Quick Study 9-9

GENERAL JOURNAL

Date	Account Titles and Explanation	PR	Debit	Credit

Quick Study 9-10

GENERAL JOURNAL

Date	Account Titles and Explanation	PR	Debit	Credit

Times Interest Earned:
_____
_____
_____

Interpretation:
_____
_____
_____
_____

Quick Study 9-12^A
_____
_____
_____
_____
_____
_____
_____
_____

Quick Study 9-13^B

GENERAL JOURNAL

Date		Account Titles and Explanation	PR	Debit	Credit

Quick Study 9-14

a. _____
_____
_____

b. _____
_____
_____
_____
_____

(1) _____		(6) _____	
(2) _____		(7) _____	
(3) _____		(8) _____	
(4) _____		(9) _____	
(5) _____		(10) _____	

Exercise 9-2

GENERAL JOURNAL

Date		Account Titles and Explanation	PR	Debit	Credit
(1)					
(2)					

GENERAL JOURNAL

Date	Account Titles and Explanation	PR	Debit	Credit
(1)				
(2)				

Exercise 9-4

(1) Maturity Date: _____

_____

_____

(2)

GENERAL JOURNAL

Date	Account Titles and Explanation	PR	Debit	Credit

(1) Maturity Date: _____

_____

_____

(2) Interest Expense (2011): _____

_____

_____

_____

(3) Interest Expense (2012): _____

_____

_____

_____

_____

(4)

GENERAL JOURNAL

Date	Account Titles and Explanation	PR	Debit	Credit

Name _____

	Subject to Tax	Rate	Tax
(a)			
FICA-Social Security..........	_____	_____	_____
FICA-Medicare.................	_____	_____	_____
FUTA............................	_____	_____	_____
SUTA............................	_____	_____	_____
(b)			
FICA-Social Security..........	_____	_____	_____
FICA-Medicare.................	_____	_____	_____
FUTA............................	_____	_____	_____
SUTA............................	_____	_____	_____
(c)			
FICA-Social Security..........	_____	_____	_____
FICA-Medicare.................	_____	_____	_____
FUTA............................	_____	_____	_____
SUTA............................	_____	_____	_____

GENERAL JOURNAL

Date		Account Titles and Explanation	PR	Debit	Credit

Exercise 9-8

GENERAL JOURNAL

Date		Account Titles and Explanation	PR	Debit	Credit

1. _____

_____

_____

_____

_____

2.

GENERAL JOURNAL

Date		Account Titles and Explanation	PR	Debit	Credit

3.

GENERAL JOURNAL

Date		Account Titles and Explanation	PR	Debit	Credit

Exercise 9-10

GENERAL JOURNAL

Date		Account Titles and Explanation	PR	Debit	Credit
(1)					
(2)					

(1) _____
_____
_____

(2) _____
_____
_____
_____

(3) _____
_____
_____

(4) _____
_____
_____
_____

(5)

GENERAL JOURNAL

Date	Account Titles and Explanation	PR	Debit	Credit

(a) _____

_____

(b) _____

_____

(c) _____

_____

(d) _____

_____

(e) _____

_____

(f) _____

_____

Analysis: _____

_____

_____

_____
_____
_____
_____
_____
_____
_____
_____
_____
_____

Exercise 9-14^B

(1)
_____
_____
_____
_____

(2)

GENERAL JOURNAL

Date		Account Titles and Explanation	PR	Debit	Credit

GENERAL JOURNAL

Date	Account Titles and Explanation	PR	Debit	Credit
(1)				
(2)				
(3)				

GENERAL JOURNAL

Date	Account Titles and Explanation	PR	Debit	Credit
(1)				
(2)				
(3)				
(4)				

a.

Employee	Cumulative Pay	Pay Subject to FICA Social Security	Pay Subject to FICA Medicare	Pay Subject to FUTA Taxes	Pay Subject to SUTA Taxes
Steve S..............	$ 6,000				
Tim V.................	60,000				
Brent G.............	87,000				
Christina S.........	156,600				
Michelle H..........	106,800				
Kathleen K.........	110,000				
Dana W.............	116,800				
Stewart M..........	36,800				
Sankha B...........	4,000				
Totals..............	$ 684,000				

b. FICA Social Security taxes

FICA Mediacare taxes

FUTA taxes

SUTA taxes

(a)

| Employee | Cumulative Pay (Excludes Current Period) | Current Period Gross Pay | | | FIT | FUTA | FICA-SS_EE | FICA-Med_EE | EE-Ben_Plan Witholding | Employee Net Pay |
		Pay Type	Pay Hours	Gross Pay	SIT	SUTA	FICA-SS_ER	FICA-Med_ER	ER-Ben_Plan Witholding	
Kathleen	$ 105,000.00	Salary	— —	$ 7,000.00	$ 2,000.00					
					300.00					
Nichole	6,800.00	Salary	— —	500.00	80.00					
					20.00					
Anthony	15,000.00	Regular	80		110.00					
		Overtime	8		25.00					
Zoey	6,500.00	Regular	80		100.00					
		Overtime	4		22.00					
Gracie	5,000.00	Regular	74	740.00	90.00					
		Overtime	0	0.00	21.00					
Totals	138,300.00				2,380.00					
					388.00					

GENERAL JOURNAL

Date	Account Titles and Explanation	PR	Debit	Credit
(b)				
(c)				
(d)				
(e)				

(1) Maturity Dates:

_____
_____
_____
_____
_____
_____
_____
_____

(2) Interest Due at Maturity:

_____
_____
_____
_____
_____
_____
_____
_____

(3) Accrued Interest at the End of 2010:

_____
_____
_____
_____
_____
_____
_____

(4) Interest Expense in 2011:

_____
_____
_____
_____
_____
_____
_____

Chapter 9   Problem 9-1A or 9-1B   Name _____
(Continued)

(5)

GENERAL JOURNAL

Date	Account Titles and Explanation	PR	Debit	Credit

Chapter 9   Problem 9-2A   Name _____

(1)

GENERAL JOURNAL

Date	Account Titles and Explanation	PR	Debit	Credit
2010				

(1) (Continued from prior page)

GENERAL JOURNAL

Date	Account Titles and Explanation	PR	Debit	Credit
2011				

(2) Warranty Expense for November 2010 and December 2010:

_____
_____
_____
_____
_____
_____

(3) Warranty Expense for January 2011:

_____
_____
_____
_____
_____

(4) Balance of the Estimated Warranty Liability as of December 31, 2010:

_____
_____
_____
_____
_____

(5) Balance of the Estimated Warranty Liability as of January 31, 2011:

_____
_____
_____
_____
_____

Name _____

(1)

GENERAL JOURNAL

Date	Account Titles and Explanation	PR	Debit	Credit
2011				

(1) (Continued from prior page)

GENERAL JOURNAL

Date	Account Titles and Explanation	PR	Debit	Credit
2012				

(2) Warranty Expense for November 2011 and December 2011:

(3) Warranty Expense for January 2012:

(4) Balance of the Estimated Warranty Liability as of December 31, 2011:

(5) Balance of the Estimated Warranty Liability as of January 31, 2012:

(1) _____ Company:

Times Interest Earned: _____

_____

_____

_____

_____

(2) _____ Company:

Times Interest Earned: _____

_____

_____

_____

_____

(3)   Sales Increase by _____ **%**

	_____ Company	_____ Company
Sales		
Variable expenses		
Income before interest		
Interest expense (fixed)		
Net Income		
Net income percent change		

(4)   Sales Increase by _____ **%**

	_____ Company	_____ Company
Sales		
Variable expenses		
Income before interest		
Interest expense (fixed)		
Net Income		
Net income percent change		

(5) Sales Increase by _____ %

	_____ Company	_____ Company
Sales		
Variable expenses		
Income before interest		
Interest expense (fixed)		
Net Income		
Net income percent change		

(6) Sales Decrease by _____ %

	_____ Company	_____ Company
Sales		
Variable expenses		
Income before interest		
Interest expense (fixed)		
Net Income		
Net income percent change		

(7) Sales Decrease by _____ %

	_____ Company	_____ Company
Sales		
Variable expenses		
Income before interest		
Interest expense (fixed)		
Net Income		
Net income percent change		

(8) Sales Decrease by _____ **%**

	_____ Company	_____ Company
Sales		
Variable expenses		
Income before interest		
Interest expense (fixed)		
Net Income		
Net income percent change		

(9) Analysis: _____

_____

_____

_____

_____

_____

_____

_____

(1) Each Employee's FICA Withholdings for Social Security:

Employee					Total
Maximum base					
Earned through _____					
Amount subject to tax					
Earned this week					
Pay subject to tax					
Tax rate					
Social Security tax					

(2) Each Employee's FICA Withholdings for Medicare:

Employee					Total
Earned this week					
Tax rate					
Medicare tax					

(3) Employer's FICA Taxes for Social Security:

Employee					Total

(4) Employer's FICA Taxes for Medicare:

Employee					Total

(5) Employer's FUTA Taxes:

Employee					**Total**
Maximum base					
Earned through _____					
Amount subject to tax					
Earned this week					
Pay subject to tax					
Tax rate					
FUTA rate					

(6) Employer's SUTA Taxes:

Employee					**Total**
Subject to tax					
Tax rate					
SUTA tax					

(7) Each Employee's Net (Take-Home) Pay:

Employee					**Total**
Gross earnings					
Less:					
FICA Soc. Sec. tax					
FICA Medicare tax					
Withholding taxes					
Health Insurance					
Take-home pay					

(8) Employer's Total Payroll-Related Expense for Each Employee:

Employee					**Total**
Gross earnings					
Plus:					
FICA Soc. Sec. tax					
FICA Medicare tax					
FUTA tax					
SUTA tax					
Health Insurance					
Pension contrib.					
Total payroll exp.					

(1)

GENERAL JOURNAL

Date	Account Titles and Explanation	PR	Debit	Credit

(2)

GENERAL JOURNAL

Date	Account Titles and Explanation	PR	Debit	Credit

(1) _____

_____

_____

_____

_____

GENERAL JOURNAL

Date	Account Titles and Explanation	PR	Debit	Credit
(2)				
(3)				
(4)				

Work Space:

Part 1

(a) Correct Ending Balance of Cash and the Amount of the Omitted Check:

_____

_____

_____

_____

_____

_____

_____

_____

_____

_____

(b) Allowance for Doubtful Accounts:

_____

_____

_____

_____

_____

_____

_____

(c) Depreciation Expense on the Truck:

_____

_____

_____

_____

_____

_____

_____

(d) Depreciation Expense on the Equipment:

_____

_____

_____

_____

_____

(e) Adjusted Revenue and Unearned Revenue Balances:

(f) Warranty Expense and Estimated Warranty Liability:

(g) Interest Payable and Interest Expense:

BUG-OFF EXTERMINATORS
December 31, 2011

Account Titles	Unadjusted Trial Balance Dr.	Unadjusted Trial Balance Cr.	Adjustments Dr.	Adjustments Cr.	Adjusted Trial Balance Dr.	Adjusted Trial Balance Cr.
Cash						
Accounts Receivable						
Allowance for Doubtful Accounts						
Merchandise Inventory						
Trucks						
Accumulated Depreciation-Trucks						
Equipment						
Accum. Depreciation-Equipment						
Accounts Payable						
Estimated Warranty Liability						
Unearned Services Revenue						
Interest Payable						
Long-Term Notes Payable						
Common Stock						
Retained Earnings						
Dividends						
Extermination Services Revenue						
Interest Revenue						
Sales						
Cost of Goods Sold						
Depreciation Expense-Trucks						
Depreciation Expense-Equipment						
Wages Expense						
Interest Expense						
Rent Expense						
Bad Debts Expense						
Miscellaneous Expense						
Repairs Expense						
Utilities Expense						
Warranty Expense						
Totals						

Part 3

GENERAL JOURNAL

Date	Account Titles and Explanation	PR	Debit	Credit

Name _____

Part 4

BUG-OFF EXTERMINATORS
Income Statement
For Year Ended December 31, 2011

BUG-OFF EXTERMINATORS
Statement of Retained Earnings
For Year Ended December 31, 2011

BUG-OFF EXTERMINATORS
Balance Sheet
December 31, 2011

(1) Times Interest Earned (2010): _____
_____
_____
_____

Times Interest Earned (2009): _____
_____
_____

Times Interest Earned (2008): _____
_____
_____
_____

Interpretation: _____
_____
_____
_____
_____

(2) _____
_____
_____
_____
_____

(3) _____
_____
_____
_____
_____

(4) FastForward: _____
_____
_____
_____
_____
_____

(1) RIM's Times Interest Earned (Current Year): _____
_____
_____

RIM's Times Interest Earned (One Year Prior): _____
_____
_____

RIM's Times Interest Earned (Two Years Prior): _____
_____
_____

Apple's Times Interest Earned (Current Year): _____
_____
_____

Apple's Times Interest Earned (One Year Prior): _____
_____
_____

Apple's Times Interest Earned (Two Years Prior): _____
_____
_____
_____

(2) Interpretation: _____
_____
_____
_____
_____

(1) _____
_____
_____
_____
_____
_____
_____
_____
_____
_____

(2) _____
_____
_____
_____
_____
_____
_____
_____
_____
_____
_____
_____
_____

MEMORANDUM

TO:

FROM:

SUBJECT:

DATE:

(1) _____
_____
_____
_____

(2) _____
_____
_____
_____

(3) _____
_____
_____
_____
_____
_____

Teamwork in Action—BTN 9-6

(1) _____
_____
_____
_____
_____

(2)

GENERAL JOURNAL

Date	Account Titles and Explanation	PR	Debit	Credit

(3) Team Discussion

(4)

GENERAL JOURNAL

Date	Account Titles and Explanation	PR	Debit	Credit

(5) Team Discussion

Part 1

Income Statement (Prospective)		
Current Operations	NEW	Total
Sales		
Cost of goods sold (30%)		
Gross profit		
Operating expenses (25%)		
Income before interest		
Interest expense		
Net income		

Part 2

Times Interest Earned:

_____

_____

_____

_____

Part 3

Income Statement (Prospective)		
Current Operations	NEW	Total
Sales		
Cost of Goods Sold (30%)		
Gross Profit		
Operating Expenses (25%)		
Income before interest		
Interest expense		
Net Income		

Times Interest Earned:

_____

_____

_____

Part 4

Income Statement (Prospective)			
	Current Operations	NEW	Total
Sales			
Cost of Goods Sold (30%)			
Gross Profit			
Operating Expenses (25%)			
Income before interest			
Interest expense			
Net Income			

Times Interest Earned: _____

_____

_____

Part 5

_____

_____

_____

_____

_____

_____

_____

_____
_____
_____
_____
_____
_____
_____
_____
_____
_____
_____
_____
_____
_____
_____
_____

Global Decision—BTN 9-9

(1) Times Interest Earned	Current Year	One Year Prior

(2) _____
_____
_____
_____
_____
_____
_____

	Date	Account Titles and Explanation	PR	Debit	Credit
(a)					
(b)					
(c)					

Name _____

GENERAL JOURNAL

Date		Account Titles and Explanation	PR	Debit	Credit

Quick Study 10-8

GENERAL JOURNAL

Date		Account Titles and Explanation	PR	Debit	Credit

(a) _____

_____

(b) _____

_____

(c) _____

_____

_____

Quick Study 10-10

Ratio Computations: _____

_____

_____

_____

_____

_____

Analysis and Interpretation: _____

_____

_____

_____

Quick Study 10-11[c]

GENERAL JOURNAL

Date		Account Titles and Explanation	PR	Debit	Credit

GENERAL JOURNAL

Date		Account Titles and Explanation	PR	Debit	Credit

Quick Study 10-13^D

GENERAL JOURNAL

Date		Account Titles and Explanation	PR	Debit	Credit

Quick Study 10-14

(a) _____

_____

(b) _____

_____

Quick Study 10-15

(a) _____

_____

(b) _____

_____

(c) _____

_____

(d) _____

_____

(1) _____

_____

_____

_____

(2)

GENERAL JOURNAL

	Date	Account Titles and Explanation	PR	Debit	Credit
(a)					
(b)					
(c)					

(3)

GENERAL JOURNAL

	Date	Account Titles and Explanation	PR	Debit	Credit
(a)					
(b)					

Name _____

(1) _____

_____

_____

_____

(2) Total Bond Interest Expense:

_____

_____

_____

_____

_____

_____

_____

_____

(3) Straight-Line Amortization Table

Semiannual Period-End	Unamortized Discount	Carrying Value
1/01/2011		
6/30/2011		
12/31/2011		
6/30/2012		
12/31/2012		
6/30/2013		
12/31/2013		

(1) _____

_____

_____

_____

(2) Total Bond Interest Expense:

_____

_____

_____

_____

_____

_____

_____

_____

_____

(3) Effective Interest Amortization Table

Semiannual Interest Period-End	(A) Cash Interest Paid (4.5% x $250,000)	(B) Bond Interest Expense [6% x Prior (E)]	(C) Discount Amortization [(B) - (A)]	(D) Unamortized Discount [Prior (D) - (C)]	(E) Carrying Value [$250,000-(D)]
1/01/2011					
6/30/2011					
12/31/2011					
6/30/2012					
12/31/2012					
6/30/2013					
12/31/2013					

(1) _____

_____

_____

_____

_____

(2) Total Bond Interest Expense:

_____

_____

_____

_____

_____

_____

_____

(3) Straight-Line Amortization Table

Semiannual Period-End	Unamortized Premium	Carrying Value
1/01/2011		
6/30/2011		
12/31/2011		
6/30/2012		
12/31/2012		
6/30/2013		
12/31/2013		

(1) Semiannual Cash Interest Payment:

_____
_____
_____
_____

(2) Number of Payments:

_____
_____
_____
_____

(3)

_____
_____
_____
_____

(4) Market Price Computation:

_____
_____
_____
_____
_____
_____
_____

(5)

GENERAL JOURNAL

Date	Account Titles and Explanation	PR	Debit	Credit

Name _____

(1) Cash proceeds from sale:

_____

_____

_____

(2) Discount at issuance:

_____

_____

_____

(3) Total Amortization for First 6 Years:

_____

_____

_____

_____

(4) Carrying value of the bonds at 12/31/2016:

_____

_____

_____

_____

(5) Purchase price:

_____

_____

(6) Loss on retirement:

_____

_____

_____

(7)

GENERAL JOURNAL

Date	Account Titles and Explanation	PR	Debit	Credit

(1) _____

_____

_____

_____

(2)

GENERAL JOURNAL

Date	Account Titles and Explanation	PR	Debit	Credit

Name _____

(1) Straight-Line Amortization Table

Semiannual Period-End	Unamortized Discount	Carrying Value
6/01/2011		
11/30/2011		
5/31/2012		
11/30/2012		
5/31/2013		
11/30/2013		
5/31/2014		
11/30/2014		
5/31/2015		

Supporting computations:

_____

_____

_____

_____

_____

_____

_____

_____

(2)

GENERAL JOURNAL

Date	Account Titles and Explanation	PR	Debit	Credit

(1) Amount of Each Payment:

_____

_____

_____

(2)

| Period Ending Date | (A) Beginning Balance [Prior (E)] | Payments | | | (E) Ending Balance [(A) - (C)] |
		(B) Debit Interest Expense + [7% x (A)]	(C) Debit Notes Payable = [(D) - (B)]	(D) Credit Cash [computed]	
2011					
2012					
2013					
2014					

GENERAL JOURNAL

Date	Account Titles and Explanation	PR	Debit	Credit

(1)(a) _____

_____

_____

_____

   (b) _____

_____

_____

_____

_____

(2) _____

_____

_____

_____

_____

_____

_____

_____

Exercise 10-17[D]

(1) _____

(2) _____

(3) _____

GENERAL JOURNAL

Date	Account Titles and Explanation	PR	Debit	Credit
(1)				
(2)				

Exercise 10-19^D

_____

_____

_____

_____

_____

_____

_____

_____

_____

_____

_____

_____

_____

GENERAL JOURNAL

Date	Account Titles and Explanation	PR	Debit	Credit
(1)				
(2)				

(3) _____

_____

_____

(4) _____

_____

_____

Part 1

(a)

Cash Flow	PV Table Value	Amount	Present Value

(b)

GENERAL JOURNAL

Date	Account Titles and Explanation	PR	Debit	Credit

Part 2

(a)

Cash Flow	PV Table Value	Amount	Present Value

(b)

GENERAL JOURNAL

Date	Account Titles and Explanation	PR	Debit	Credit

Part 3

(a)

Cash Flow	PV Table Value	Amount	Present Value

(b)

GENERAL JOURNAL

Date	Account Titles and Explanation	PR	Debit	Credit

Problem 10-2A or 10-2B

Part 1

GENERAL JOURNAL

Date	Account Titles and Explanation	PR	Debit	Credit

Part 2

(a) Cash Payment: _____
_____

(b) Semiannual Amortization: _____
_____
_____

(c) Bond Interest Expense: _____
_____
_____

Part 3

Total Bond Interest Expense: _____
_____
_____
_____
_____
_____

Part 4 Straight-Line Amortization Table

Semiannual Period-End	Unamortized Discount	Carrying Value
1/01/2011		
6/30/2011		
12/31/2011		
6/30/2012		
12/31/2012		

Part 5

GENERAL JOURNAL

Date	Account Titles and Explanation	PR	Debit	Credit

Problem 10-3A or 10-3B

Part 1

GENERAL JOURNAL

Date	Account Titles and Explanation	PR	Debit	Credit

Part 2

(a) Cash Payment: _____

_____

(b) Semiannual Amortization: _____

_____

_____

(c) Bond Interest Expense: _____

_____

_____

Part 3

Total Bond Interest Expense: _____

_____
_____
_____
_____
_____
_____
_____
_____
_____

Part 4 Straight-Line Amortization Table

Semiannual Period-End	Unamortized Premium	Carrying Value
1/01/2011		
6/30/2011		
12/31/2011		
6/30/2012		
12/31/2012		

Part 5

GENERAL JOURNAL

Date	Account Titles and Explanation	PR	Debit	Credit

Part 1

Total Bond Interest Expense:

_____
_____
_____
_____
_____
_____
_____
_____
_____

Part 2 Straight-Line Amortization Table

Semiannual Interest Period-End	Unamortized Premium	Carrying Value
1/01/2011		
6/30/2011		
12/31/2011		
6/30/2012		
12/31/2012		
6/30/2013		
12/31/2013		
6/30/2014		
12/31/2014		
6/30/2015		
12/31/2015		

Part 3

GENERAL JOURNAL

Date	Account Titles and Explanation	PR	Debit	Credit

Chapter 10   Problem 10-5A^B or 10-5B^B   *Name* _____

Part 1

Total Bond Interest Expense: _____
_____
_____
_____
_____
_____
_____
_____
_____
_____
_____

Part 2 Effective Interest Amortization Table

Semiannual Interest Period-End	(A) Cash Interest Paid [__% x $____]	(B) Bond Interest Expense [__% x Prior (E)]	(C) Premium Amortization [(A) - (B)]	(D) Unamortized Premium [Prior (D) - (C)]	(E) Carrying Value [$____ + (D)]
1/01/2011					
6/30/2011					
12/31/2011					
6/30/2012					
12/31/2012					
6/30/2013					
12/31/2013					
6/30/2014					
12/31/2014					
6/30/2015					
12/31/2015					

Part 3

GENERAL JOURNAL

Date	Account Titles and Explanation	PR	Debit	Credit

Part 4

Cash Flow	PV Table Value	Amount	Present Value

Comparison to Part 2 Table:

_____

_____

_____

_____

_____

_____

_____

Chapter 10   Problem 10-6A or 10-6B   *Name* _____

Part 1

GENERAL JOURNAL

Date		Account Titles and Explanation	PR	Debit	Credit

Part 2

Total Bond Interest Expense: _____

_____
_____
_____
_____
_____
_____
_____

Part 3   Straight-Line Amortization Table

Semiannual Interest Period-End	Unamortized Discount	Carrying Value
1/01/2011		
6/30/2011		
12/31/2011		
6/30/2012		
12/31/2012		

Part 4

GENERAL JOURNAL

Date		Account Titles and Explanation	PR	Debit	Credit

Part 5 (for Problem 10-6A only)

_____
_____
_____
_____
_____
_____
_____
_____
_____
_____
_____
_____
_____
_____
_____
_____
_____
_____
_____
_____
_____

Chapter 10   Problem 10-7A^B or 10-7B^B *Name* _____

Part 1

GENERAL JOURNAL

Date		Account Titles and Explanation	PR	Debit	Credit

Part 2

Total Bond Interest Expense: _____

_____
_____
_____
_____
_____
_____
_____
_____

Part 3 Effective Interest Amortization Table

Semiannual Interest Period-End	(A) Cash Interest Paid [_% x $___]	(B) Bond Interest Expense [_% x Prior (E)]	(C) Discount Amortization [(B) - (A)]	(D) Unamortized Discount [Prior (D) - (C)]	(E) Carrying Value [$___ - (D)]
1/01/2011					
6/30/2011					
12/31/2011					
6/30/2012					
12/31/2012					

Part 4

GENERAL JOURNAL

Date		Account Titles and Explanation	PR	Debit	Credit

Part 1

GENERAL JOURNAL

Date	Account Titles and Explanation	PR	Debit	Credit

Part 2

Total Bond Interest Expense: _____

_____

_____

_____

_____

_____

_____

_____

_____

Part 3 Effective Interest Amortization Table

Semiannual Interest Period-End	(A) Cash Interest Paid [% x $]	(B) Bond Interest Expense [% x Prior (E)]	(C) Premium Amortization [(A) - (B)]	(D) Unamortized Premium [Prior (D) - (C)]	(E) Carrying Value [$_____ + (D)]
1/01/2011					
6/30/2011					
12/31/2011					
6/30/2012					
12/31/2012					

Part 4

GENERAL JOURNAL

Date	Account Titles and Explanation	PR	Debit	Credit

Part 5

GENERAL JOURNAL

Date	Account Titles and Explanation	PR	Debit	Credit

Part 6

_____

_____

_____

_____

_____

_____

_____

_____

Part 1

Amount of Each Payment:

_____

_____
_____
_____
_____
_____
_____
_____

Part 2

	(A)	Payments			(E)
		(B)	(C)	(D)	
		Debit	Debit		
Period	Beginning	Interest	Notes	Credit	Ending
Ending	Balance	Expense +	Payable =	Cash	Balance
Date	[Prior (E)]	[___% x (A)]	[(D) - (B)]	[computed]	[(A) - (C)]

_____

_____

_____

_____

_____

_____

Part 3

GENERAL JOURNAL

Date		Account Titles and Explanation	PR	Debit	Credit

Problem 10-10A or 10-10B

Part 1

_____ **Company—Debt-to-Equity Ratio:** _____
_____
_____
_____
_____

_____ **Company—Debt-to-Equity Ratio:** _____
_____
_____
_____
_____

Part 2

Analysis and Interpretation: _____
_____
_____
_____
_____
_____

Part 1

Present Value of the Lease Payments: _____

_____

_____

_____

Part 2

GENERAL JOURNAL

Date	Account Titles and Explanation	PR	Debit	Credit

Part 3

Capital Lease Liability Payment (Amortization) Schedule:

Period Ending Date	Beginning Balance of Lease Liability	Interest on Lease Liability (__%)	Reduction of Lease Liability	Cash Lease Payment	Ending Balance of Lease Liability
Year 1					
Year 2					
Year 3					
Year 4					
Year 5					

Part 4

GENERAL JOURNAL

Date	Account Titles and Explanation	PR	Debit	Credit

Part 1

Maximum Loan Allowed: _____

_____
_____
_____
_____
_____
_____
_____
_____
_____
_____

Part 2

(a) Percent of Assets Financed by Debt _____

_____
_____
_____

(b) Percent of Assets Financed by Equity _____

_____
_____
_____
_____

Part 3

_____
_____
_____
_____
_____
_____

(1) _____

_____

_____

_____

_____

_____

_____

_____

_____

_____

_____

(2) _____

_____

_____

_____

(3) _____

_____

_____

_____

(4) Fast Forward: _____

_____

_____

_____

_____

_____

_____

Name _____

(1) RIM

       Current Year:

_____

_____

_____

       Prior Year:

_____

_____

_____

   Apple

       Current Year:

_____

_____

_____

       Prior Year:

_____

_____

_____

(2) _____

_____

_____

_____

_____

Chapter 10 **Ethics Challenge** ***Name*** ______________________
BTN 10-3

(1)

(2)

MEMORANDUM

TO:
FROM:
DATE:
SUBJECT:

(1) Long Term Liabilities:

_____

_____

_____

_____

_____

_____

(2a)

_____

_____

_____

_____

_____

(2b)

_____

_____

_____

_____

_____

Parts 1 & 2

_____
_____
_____
_____
_____
_____
_____
_____
_____
_____
_____
_____
_____
_____
_____
_____
_____
_____

Part 3

_____
_____
_____
_____
_____
_____
_____
_____
_____
_____

Part 4

_____
_____
_____
_____
_____
_____

Part 5

Similarities	Differences

Part 1

	Current	Alternative Notes for Expansion				
		10% Note	15% Note	16% Note	17% Note	20% Note
Income before interest.............						
Interest expense.						
Net income.........						
Equity................						
Return on equity.						

Work Space: _____
_____
_____
_____

Part 2

_____
_____
_____
_____
_____
_____
_____
_____
_____
_____

_____

_____
_____
_____
_____
_____
_____
_____
_____
_____
_____

Global Decision—BTN 10-9

(1) Current Year Ratio:

_____
_____
_____

  Prior Year Ratio:

_____
_____
_____

(2) _____

_____
_____
_____
_____
_____

Name _____

Price-Earnings Ratio

_____
_____
_____

Analysis

_____
_____
_____

Quick Study 11-15

Dividend Yield

_____
_____

Analysis

_____
_____
_____

Quick Study 11-16

_____
_____
_____
_____
_____
_____
_____

Quick Study 11-17

GENERAL JOURNAL

Date	Account Titles and Explanation	PR	Debit	Credit

	Characteristic	Corporations
1	Duration of Life	
2	Owner liability	
3	Legal status	
4	Tax status of income	
5	Owner authority & control	
6	Ease of formation	
7	Transferability of ownership	
8	Ability to raise large amounts of capital	

Exercise 11-2

GENERAL JOURNAL

Date	Account Titles and Explanation	PR	Debit	Credit
(1)				
(2)				
(3)				

Name _____

Part 1
(a) Retained Earnings:
_____
_____
_____
_____

(b) Total Stockholders' Equity:
_____
_____
_____
_____
_____

(c) Number of Outstanding Shares:
_____
_____
_____
_____

Part 2
(a) Retained Earnings:
_____
_____
_____
_____

(b) Total Stockholders' Equity:
_____
_____
_____
_____
_____

(c) Number of Outstanding Shares:
_____
_____
_____
_____

Part 3
_____
_____
_____
_____
_____

Part 1

GENERAL JOURNAL

Date	Account Titles and Explanation	PR	Debit	Credit

Part 2

	Before	After

Part 3

	Feb. 5	Feb. 28

Part 2

Changes to the equity section include:

_____
_____
_____
_____
_____
_____
_____
_____
_____
_____
_____
_____
_____
_____
_____
_____
_____
_____
_____
_____
_____

Revised Stockholders' Equity Section (for support of your part 2 solution):

Name _____

_____ COMPANY
Statement of Retained Earnings
For Year Ended December 31, 2011

_____

_____

_____

_____

_____

_____

_____

_____

_____

_____

Exercise 11-12

(1) Net Income Available to Common Stockholders: _____

_____

_____

_____

_____

(2) Basic Earnings per Share:

_____

_____

_____

_____

Name _____

(1) Net Income Available to Common Stockholders:

_____
_____
_____
_____

(2) Basic Earnings per Share:

_____
_____
_____
_____

Exercise 11-14

Dividend Yield:

(1) _____

(2) _____

(3) _____

(4) _____
_____

Analysis:

_____
_____

Exercise 11-15

Price-Earnings Ratio:

(1) _____

(2) _____

(3) _____

(4) _____

Analysis:

_____

(1) _____

_____
_____
_____
_____
_____
_____
_____
_____
_____
_____

(2) _____

_____
_____
_____
_____
_____
_____
_____
_____
_____

Exercise 11-17

(1) _____

_____
_____
_____

(2)   **GENERAL JOURNAL**

Date		Account Titles and Explanation	PR	Debit	Credit

(3) _____

_____
_____
_____

(1)

GENERAL JOURNAL

Date	Account Titles and Explanation	PR	Debit	Credit

(2)

_____ CORPORATION

Statement of Retained Earnings

For Year Ended December 31, 2012

(3)

_____ CORPORATION

Stockholders' Equity Section of the Balance Sheet

December 31, 2012

Part 2

_____

_____CORPORATION

Statement of Retained Earnings

For Year Ended December 31, 2012

_____
_____
_____
_____
_____
_____
_____
_____

Part 3

_____

_____CORPORATION

Stockholders' Equity Section of the Balance Sheet

December 31, 2012

_____
_____
_____
_____
_____
_____
_____
_____

Part 1

	Explanations for each of the entries:
Oct. 2 (Jan.17)*	
Oct. 25 (Feb. 5)*	
Oct. 31 (Feb. 28)*	
Nov. 5 (Mar. 14)*	
Dec. 1 (Mar. 25)*	
Dec. 31 (Mar. 31)*	

*Dates for Problem 11-3B are in parentheses.

Part 2

	Oct. 2 (Jan. 17)*	Oct. 25 (Feb. 5)*	Oct. 31 (Feb. 28)*	Nov. 5 (Mar. 14)*	Dec. 1 (Mar. 25)*	Dec. 31 (Mar. 31)*
Common stock............						
Common stock dividend distributable..						
Paid-In capital in excess of par.............						
Retained earnings..........						
Total equity..................						

*Dates for Problem 11-3B are in parentheses.

Part 1
Outstanding Common Shares:

_____

_____

_____

_____

_____

Part 2
Cash Dividend Amounts:

_____

_____

_____

_____

Part 3
Capitalization of Retained Earnings:

_____

_____

_____

_____

_____

Part 4
Cost Per Share of Treasury Stock:

_____

_____

_____

Part 5
Net Income Computation:

_____

_____

_____

_____

_____

_____

_____

(1) Market Price Per Share: _____

_____

_____

_____

(2) Computation of Stock Par Values: _____

_____

_____

_____

_____

(3) Book Value Per Preferred Share: _____

_____

_____

   Book Value Per Common Share: _____

_____

_____

_____

_____

(4) Book Value Per Preferred Share: _____

_____

_____

_____

   Book Value Per Common Share: _____

_____

_____

_____

_____

_____

_____

(5) Book Value Per Preferred Share:

_____
_____
_____
_____
_____

Book Value Per Common Share:

_____
_____
_____
_____
_____
_____
_____
_____

(6) _____

_____
_____
_____
_____
_____
_____
_____
_____

(7) _____

_____
_____
_____
_____
_____

(1a)   GENERAL JOURNAL

Date		Account Titles and Explanation	PR	Debit	Credit

(1b)   GENERAL JOURNAL

Date		Account Titles and Explanation	PR	Debit	Credit

(1c)   GENERAL JOURNAL

Date		Account Titles and Explanation	PR	Debit	Credit

(2)   (a) _____

_____

_____

_____

(b) _____

_____

_____

(c) _____

_____

_____

(3) _____

_____

_____

_____

(1) _____

_____

_____

_____

_____

_____

_____

_____

(2) _____

_____

_____

_____

_____

(3) _____

_____

_____

_____

(4) _____

_____

_____

_____

(5) _____

_____

_____

(6) FastForward: _____

_____

_____

_____

(1)
RIM Book Value Per Common Share: _____
_____

Palm Book Value Per Common Share: _____
_____

Apple Book Value Per Common Share: _____
_____

(2)
RIM Earnings Per Share: _____
_____

Palm Earnings per Share: _____
_____

Apple Earnings per Share: _____
_____

(3)
RIM Dividend Yield: _____
_____

Palm Dividend Yield: _____
_____

Apple Dividend Yield: _____
_____

Analysis: _____
_____
_____
_____

(4)

RIM Price-Earnings Ratio: _____

_____

Palm Price-Earnings Ratio: _____

_____

Apple Price-Earnings Ratio: _____

_____

Analysis & Interpretation: _____

_____

_____

_____

_____

_____

_____

_____

_____

_____

_____

_____

_____

_____

_____

_____

_____

_____

_____

_____

_____

_____

_____

_____

_____

_____

_____

_____

_____

_____

_____

_____

_____

_____

_____

_____

_____

_____

_____

_____

MEMORANDUM

TO:
FROM:
DATE:
SUBJECT:

Company	Earnings Per Share	Market Price of Stock	Price-Earnings Ratio

Industry Norm:

Meaning of Price-Earnings Ratio:

Comparison Across Companies:

Concluding Analysis:

Part 1

_____
_____
_____

Part 2

_____
_____
_____

Part 3

_____
_____
_____
_____

Part 4

_____
_____
_____
_____

Teamwork in Action—BTN 11-6

Part 1
(a) Impact on Financial Position due to Stock Buyback:

_____
_____
_____
_____
_____
_____

(b) Reasons for Stock Buyback:

_____
_____
_____
_____
_____

Part 2

GENERAL JOURNAL

Date	Account Titles and Explanation	PR	Debit	Credit
Reacquisition entry				
(a)				
(b)				
(c)				
(d)				
(e)				

Part 3

Similarities: _____

_____

_____

Differences: _____

_____

_____

Name _____

Part 1

	Plan A	Plan B

Part 2

	Plan A	Plan B

Part 3

_____
_____
_____
_____
_____
_____
_____
_____
_____
_____

Global Decision—BTN 11-9

(1) Book Value per Common Share
_____
_____
_____
_____
_____
_____
_____

(2) Earnings per Share
_____
_____
_____
_____
_____
_____
_____

(3) Analysis
_____
_____
_____
_____
_____
_____

Chapter 12   Quick Study 12-1   *Name* _____

(1) _____   (6) _____
(2) _____   (7) _____
(3) _____   (8) _____
(4) _____   (9) _____
(5) _____   (10) _____

Quick Study 12-2

(1) _____
_____
_____
_____

(2) _____
_____
_____
_____

(3) _____
_____
_____
_____

(4) _____
_____
_____

Quick Study 12-3

Cash Flows from Operating Activities
_____
_____
_____
_____
_____
_____
_____
_____
_____
_____

_____
_____
_____
_____
_____
_____
_____
_____

Krug, Inc.
Statement of Cash Flows (Indirect Method)
For Year Ended June 30, 20___

_____
_____
_____
_____
_____
_____
_____
_____
_____
_____
_____
_____
_____
_____
_____
_____
_____
_____
_____

Supporting calculations:

(2) _____
_____
_____
_____

(1) _____

Cash Flow	U.S. GAAP	IFRS
(2) a.		
b.		
c.		
d.		

Exercise 12-1

Cash Flow from Operating Activities

_____
_____
_____
_____
_____
_____
_____
_____
_____
_____
_____

		Statement of Cash Flows		Noncash Investing & Financing Activities	Not Reported on Statement or in Note
		Operating Activities	Investing Activities	Financing Activities	
a.	Accounts receivable decreased this year.					
b.	Purchased land by issuing stock.					
c.	Paid cash to purchase inventory.					
d.	Sold equipment for cash, yielding a loss.					
e.	Accounts payable decreased this year.					
f.	Income taxes payable increased this year.					
g.	Declared and paid a cash dividend.					
h.	Recorded depreciation expense.					
i.	Paid cash to settle long-term notes payable.					
j.	Prepaid expenses increased this year.					

		Statement of Cash Flows		Noncash Investing & Financing Activities	Not Reported on Statement or in Note
	Operating Activities	Investing Activities	Financing Activities		
a. Accepted six-month note receivable in exchange for plant assets.					
b. Recorded depreciation expense.					
c. Paid cash to acquire treasury stock.					
d. Collected cash from sales.					
e. Borrowed cash from bank by signing a 9-month note payable.					
f. Paid cash to purchase patent.					
g. Retired long-term notes payable by issuing stock.					
h. Paid cash toward accounts payable.					
i. Sold inventory for cash.					
j. Paid cash dividend that was declared in a prior period.					

Cash Flows from Operating Activities

Exercise 12-5^B

Case A

Case B

Case C

Name _____

Cash Flows from Operating Activities

_____
_____
_____
_____
_____
_____
_____
_____
_____
_____
_____

<u>Supporting computations:</u>

Exercise 12-7[B]

Cash Flows from Operating Activities

_____
_____
_____
_____
_____
_____
_____
_____

<u>Supporting computations:</u>

Name _____

Cash Flows from Investing Activities

_____
_____
_____
_____
_____
_____
_____
_____

Exercise 12-9

Cash Flows for Financing Activities

_____
_____
_____
_____
_____
_____
_____
_____

_____, Inc.

Statement of Cash Flows (Indirect Method)

For Year Ended June 30, 20____

Supporting Computations for:

(1) Cash received from sale of equipment:

Cash paid for new equipment:

Part 1

Supporting computations continued.

(2) Cash paid to retire notes: _____

_____

_____

_____

(3) Cash paid for dividends: _____

_____

_____

_____

Part 2

Cash Flow on Total Assets Ratio: _____

_____

_____

Interpretation: _____

_____

_____

Chapter 12   Exercise 12-11^B   **Name** _____

_____, Inc.
Statement of Cash Flows (Direct Method)
For Year Ended June 30, 20___

Supporting Computations for:

(1) Cash received from customers:

(2) Cash paid for merchandise inventory:

Part 1

Supporting Computations Continued.

(3) Cash paid for other operating expenses:

_____

_____

_____

(4) Cash paid for income taxes:

_____

_____

(5) Cash received from sale of equipment:

_____

_____

_____

   Cash paid for new equipment:

_____

_____

_____

(6) Cash paid to retire notes:

_____

_____

(7) Cash paid for dividends:

_____

_____

_____

Name _____

_____ **COMPANY**
Statement of Cash Flows
For Year Ended December 31, 20___

Footnotes:

Part 1

_____ CORPORATION
Statement of Cash Flows
For Year Ended December 31, 20___

Part 2

(a)

(b)

(c)

(d)

Name _____

Cash Flows from Operating Activities

_____

_____

_____

_____

_____

_____

_____

_____

_____

_____

_____

Exercise 12-15

(1) Cash Flows from Operating Activities

_____

_____

_____

_____

_____

_____

_____

_____

_____

_____

_____

_____

(2) _____

_____

_____

_____

_____

(3) _____

_____

_____

_____

2010 _____

_____

_____

2011 _____

_____

_____

Interpretation: _____

_____

_____

Spreadsheet for Statement of Cash Flows
For Year Ended December 31, 20___

	Dec. 31, 2010	Analysis of changes Debit	Credit	Dec. 31, 2011
Balance sheet-debit bal. accounts:				
Cash...				
Accounts receivable.......................				
Merchandise inventory...................				
Plant assets....................................				
Balance sheet-credit bal. accounts:				
Accum. depreciation-Plant assets				
Accounts payable....................				
Notes payable..........................				
Long-term notes payable..........				
Common Stock.........................				
Retained earnings...................				
Statement of cash flows:				
Operating activities				
Net income..............................				
_____ in accts. receivable...				
_____ in merch. inventory...				
_____ in accounts payable...				
Depreciation expense..............				
Investing activities				
Payment for plant assets..............				
Financing activities				
Payments of cash dividends.....				
Issued note payable...................				

_____

Statement of Cash Flows
For Year Ended December 31, 20___

Part 1

_____
Statement of Cash Flows
For Year Ended December 31, 20____

_____
_____
_____
_____
_____
_____
_____
_____
_____
_____
_____
_____
_____
_____
_____
_____
_____
_____
_____
_____
_____
_____
_____

Statement Footnotes:

_____
_____
_____

Supporting calculations:

Part 2

_____
_____
_____
_____
_____
_____
_____
_____
_____
_____
_____
_____
_____
_____

Chapter 12 Problem 12-2A[B] or 12-2B[B] *Name* ______________________

____

Statement of Cash Flows

For Year Ended December 31, 20____

Statement Footnotes:

Supporting calculations:

| | **Spreadsheet for Statement of Cash Flows** | | | |
| | **For Year Ended December 31, 20___** | | | |

| | | Analysis of changes | | |
| | _Dec. 31, 2010_ | _Debit_ | _Credit_ | _Dec. 31, 2011_ |

Balance sheet-debit bal. accounts:
  Cash...
  Accounts receivable.......................
  Merchandise inventory...................
  Prepaid expenses..........................
  Equipment.....................................

Balance sheet-credit bal. accounts:
  Accum. depreciation-Equip.......
  Accounts payable....................
  Short-term notes payable.........
  Long-term notes payable..........
  Common Stock, $___par value...
  Paid-in capital in excess of
    par value, common stock.......
  Retained earnings...................

Statement of cash flows:
Operating activities
  Net income................................
  _____ in accts. receivable...
  _____ in merch. inventory...
  _____ in prepaid expenses...
  _____ in accounts payable...
  Depreciation expense...............
  _____ on sale of equipment..
Investing activities
  Receipt from sale of equipment...
  Payment to purchase equipment..
Financing activities
  Borrowed on short-term note....
  Payment on long-term note......
  Issued common stock for cash..
  Payments of cash dividends.....

**Noncash investing and financing
activities:**
  Purchase of equip. financed
  by long-term note payable.....

_____

Statement of Cash Flows
For Year Ended December 31, 20___

Supporting calculations:

	Spreadsheet for Statement of Cash Flows			
	For Year Ended December 31, 20___			
		Analysis of changes		
	Dec. 31, 2010	*Debit*	*Credit*	*Dec. 31, 2011*
Balance sheet-debit bal. accounts:				
Cash..				
Accounts receivable.........................				
Merchandise inventory.....................				
Equipment......................................				
Balance sheet-credit bal. accounts:				
Accum. depreciation-Equip...............				
Accounts payable............................				
Income taxes payable......................				
Common stock, $___par value...........				
Paid-in capital in excess of				
par value, common stock...........				
Retained earnings..				
Statement of cash flows:				
Operating activities				
Net income......................................				
_____ in accts. receivable..........				
_____ in merch. inventory..........				
_____ in accounts payable.........				
_____ in income taxes payable...				
Depreciation expense....................				
Investing activities				
Payment for equipment....................				
Financing activities				
Issued common stock for cash..........				
Paid cash dividends.........................				

_____

_____
Statement of Cash Flows
For Year Ended December 31, 20___
_____

_____

_____

_____

_____

_____

_____

_____

_____

_____

_____

_____

_____

_____

_____

_____

_____

_____

_____

_____

_____

_____

_____

_____

_____

_____

_____

_____

_____

_____

Supporting calculations:

Chapter 12 Problem 12-7A or 12-7B *Name* ____________________

Cash Flows from Operating Activities—Indirect Method

Problem 12-8A[B] or 12-8B[B]

Cash Flows from Operating Activities—Direct Method

(1)   RIM's Cash Flow on Total Assets Ratio:

      Current Year

_____

_____

      Prior Year

_____

     Apple's Cash Flow on Total Assets Ratio:

      Current Year

_____

      Prior Year

_____

_____

(2) _____

_____

_____

_____

_____

(3) _____

_____

_____

_____

_____

(4) _____

_____

_____

_____

_____

Name _____

(1) (a) _____

_____

_____

_____

(b) _____

_____

_____

_____

_____

_____

(2) _____

_____

_____

_____

_____

_____

_____

_____

_____

_____

_____

_____

_____

MEMORANDUM

TO:

FROM:

DATE:

SUBJECT:

---

(1) _____
_____
_____

(2) _____
_____
_____

(3)	2008	2009	2010
Net income (net loss)			
Cash flow from operations			

Analysis: _____
_____
_____

(4) _____
_____
_____

(5) _____
_____

(6) _____
_____
_____
_____

Teamwork in Action—BTN 12-6

Part 1

(a) _____
_____
_____
_____

Part 1   (Continued)

(b)   **Similarities**   **Differences**

_____
_____
_____
_____
_____
_____
_____
_____

(c) _____
_____
_____
_____
_____
_____
_____
_____
_____

(d) _____
_____
_____
_____
_____
_____
_____

Part 2

Adjusting Net Income to Cash Flow from Operating Activities	
Items to Add	**Items to Subtract**
a.	
b.	
c.	
d.	

Part 3

(a) _____

_____

_____

_____

_____

_____

_____

(b) _____

_____

_____

_____

_____

_____

_____

_____

_____

_____

(c) _____

_____

_____

_____

_____

_____

_____

_____

(d) _____

_____

_____

_____

_____

_____

_____

(1) _____

_____

_____

_____

_____

_____

_____

_____

_____

(2) _____

_____

_____

_____

_____

_____

_____

_____

_____

_____

MEMORANDUM

TO:
FROM:
DATE:
SUBJECT:

(1) _____
_____
_____
_____

(2) _____
_____
_____
_____
_____
_____
_____

(3) _____
_____
_____
_____

Global Decision—BTN 12-10

(1) Cash Flow on Total Assets Ratio
    Current Year:
_____
_____
_____

    Prior Year:
_____
_____
_____

(2) Comparative Analysis:
_____
_____
_____
_____
_____
_____

Not part of General-Purpose Statements: _____
_____
_____
_____
_____

Quick Study 13-2

_____
_____
_____
_____
_____
_____
_____
_____
_____
_____
_____
_____
_____
_____
_____
_____

Quick Study 13-3

Trend Percents _____
      2011 _____
      2010 _____

Quick Study 13-4

Common-Size Percents _____
      2011 _____
      2010 _____

Account	2011	2010	Dollar Change	Percent Change

Quick Study 13-6

Ratio	2011	2010	Change
1. Profit Margin Ratio	8%	6%	
2. Debt Ratio	45%	40%	
3. Gross Margin Ratio	33%	45%	
4. Acid-Test Ratio	0.99	1.10	
5. Accounts Receivable Turnover	5.4	6.6	
6. Basic Earnings Per Share	$1.24	$1.20	
7. Inventory Turnover	3.5	3.3	
8. Dividend Yield	1.0%	0.8%	

COMPARATIVE ANALYSIS REPORT

Quick Study 13-8[A]

(a) _____

_____

_____

_____

_____

(b) _____

_____

_____

_____

_____

_____

_____

_____

_____

_____

_____

_____

Exercise 13-1

(1)	_____	(6)	_____
(2)	_____	(7)	_____
(3)	_____	(8)	_____
(4)	_____	(9)	_____
(5)	_____	(10)	_____

Exercise 13-2

(1) _____

(2) _____

(3) _____

_____

Account	2013	2012	2011	2010	2009

Analysis:

_____

_____

_____

_____

_____

_____

_____

Exercise 13-4

Answer:

_____

_____

_____

Supporting Work:

_____

_____

_____

_____

_____

_____

_____

_____

_____

_____

_____

_____

_____

Account	2011	2010

Analysis: _____

_____

_____

_____

_____

_____

Exercise 13-6

COMPARATIVE ANALYSIS REPORT

_____ Company Common-Size Comparative Balance Sheets December 31, 2010-2012	2012	2011	2010

Analysis and interpretation:

(1) Current Ratio:
2012: _____

_____
_____

2011: _____

_____
_____

2010: _____

_____
_____
_____

(2) Acid-test ratio:
2012: _____

_____
_____

2011: _____

_____
_____

2010: _____

_____
_____
_____

Analysis and interpretation: _____

_____
_____
_____
_____
_____
_____

Name _____

1. Days' sales uncollected:
2012: _____

_____

2011: _____

_____

_____

2. Accounts receivable turnover:
2012: _____

_____

2011: _____

_____

_____

3. Inventory turnover:
2012: _____

_____

2011: _____

_____

_____

4. Days' sales in inventory:
2012: _____

_____

2011: _____

_____

Analysis and interpretation:

_____

_____

_____

_____

_____

_____

Name _____

(1)

Debt Ratio and Equity Ratio	2012	2011

(2) Debt-to-Equity Ratio

(3) Times Interest Earned

Analysis and interpretation:

(1) Profit margin:

2012: _____

_____

_____

2011: _____

_____

_____

_____

(2) Total asset turnover:

2012: _____

_____

_____

2011: _____

_____

_____

_____

(3) Return on total assets:

2012: _____

_____

_____

2011: _____

_____

_____

_____

Analysis and interpretation:

_____

_____

_____

_____

_____

_____

_____

_____

(1) Return on common stockholders' equity:

2012:

_____

_____

_____

2011:

_____

_____

_____

(2) Price-earnings ratio, December 31:

2012:

_____

_____

_____

2011:

_____

_____

_____

(3) Dividend yield:

2012:

_____

_____

_____

2011:

_____

_____

_____

Analysis and interpretation:

_____

_____

_____

_____

_____

_____

_____

(1) _____	(5) _____
(2) _____	(6) _____
(3) _____	(7) _____
(4) _____	(8) _____

Exercise 13-14^A

| _____ Merchandising |
| Income Statement |
| For Year Ended December 31, 20____ |

_____

_____

_____

_____

_____

_____

_____

_____

_____

_____

_____

_____

_____

_____

_____

_____

Exercise 13-15

1. Current ratio: _____

_____

Net profit margin _____

_____

Sales-to-assets: _____

_____

2. _____

_____

Part 1

Current Ratio:

2012: _____

_____

2011: _____

_____

2010: _____

_____

_____

Part 2

Common-Size Comparative Income Statements For Years Ended December 31, 2012, 2011, and 2010			
	2012	2011	2010

_____

_____

_____

_____

_____

_____

_____

_____

_____

_____

_____

_____

_____

Part 3

Balance Sheet Data in Trend Percents December 31, 2012, 2011, and 2010			
	2012	2011	2010
_____	_____	_____	_____
_____	_____	_____	_____
_____	_____	_____	_____
_____	_____	_____	_____
_____	_____	_____	_____
_____	_____	_____	_____
_____	_____	_____	_____
_____	_____	_____	_____
_____	_____	_____	_____
_____	_____	_____	_____
_____	_____	_____	_____
_____	_____	_____	_____
_____	_____	_____	_____

Part 4

Significant relations revealed: _____

_____

_____

_____

_____

_____

_____

_____

_____

_____

_____

_____

_____

_____

_____

Part 1

Income Statement Trends							
For Years Ended December 31, 2012-2006							
	2012	*2011*	*2010*	*2009*	*2008*	*2007*	*2006*

Balance Sheet Trends							
December 31, 2012-2006							
	2012	*2011*	*2010*	*2009*	*2008*	*2007*	*2006*

Part 2

Analysis and interpretation: _____

_____

_____

_____

_____

_____

_____

_____

_____

_____

_____

_____

_____

_____

_____

_____

_____

Transaction	Current Assets	Quick Assets	Current Liabilities	Current Ratio	Acid-Test Ratio	Working Capital
Beg. Bal.						
End. Bal.						

Supporting computations:

(1) Current ratio:

_____

_____

_____

(2) Acid-test ratio:

_____

_____

_____

(3) Days' sales uncollected:

_____

_____

_____

(4) Inventory turnover:

_____

_____

_____

(5) Days' sales in inventory:

_____

_____

_____

(6) Debt-to-equity ratio:

_____

_____

_____

(7) Times interest earned:

_____

_____

_____

(8) Profit margin ratio:

_____

_____

_____

_____

(9) Total asset turnover: _____

_____

_____

_____

_____

(10) Return on total assets: _____

_____

_____

_____

_____

(11) Return on common stockholders' equity: _____

_____

_____

_____

_____

Part 1

		Company		Company

a. Current ratio:

_____

_____

_____

b. Acid-test ratio:

_____

_____

_____

c. Accounts (incl. notes) receivable turnover:

_____

_____

_____

_____

d. Inventory turnover:

_____

_____

_____

e. Days' sales in inventory:

_____

_____

_____

f. Days' sales uncollected:

_____

_____

_____

Short-term credit risk analysis:

_____

_____

_____

_____

Part 2

	Company	Company
a. Profit margin ratio:		
b. Total asset turnover:		
c. Return on total assets:		
d. Return on common stockholders' equity:		
e. Price-earnings ratio:		
f. Dividend yield:		
Investment analysis:		

Part 1 Effect of Income Taxes:

Items	Pretax	___% Tax Effect	After-Tax

Part 2 Income from Continuing Operations (and its Components):

(1) Trend Percents for selected income statement accounts:

	2010	2009	2008
Revenues			
Cost of Goods Sold			
Operating expenses			
Income taxes			
Net income			

(2) Common-size percents for asset categories and accounts:

	2010	2009
Total current assets		
Property and equipment, net		
Intangible assets		

(3) Analysis and Interpretation:

_____
_____
_____
_____
_____
_____
_____
_____
_____
_____
_____
_____
_____

(4) FastForward

_____
_____
_____
_____
_____
_____
_____
_____

(1)

Key figures	Research In Motion Percent	Apple Amount
Cash and cash equivalents		
Accounts receivable, net		
Inventories		
Retained earnings		
Cost of sales		
Revenues		
Total Assets		

(2)

_____

_____

_____

_____

(3)

_____

_____

_____

_____

_____

(4)

_____

_____

_____

_____

_____

_____

(1) _____
_____
_____
_____
_____
_____
_____
_____
_____
_____

(2) _____
_____
_____
_____
_____
_____
_____
_____
_____
_____
_____
_____
_____
_____
_____
_____

MEMORANDUM
TO:
FROM:
DATE:
SUBJECT:

	2008	2009

1. Profit margin ratio

_____

_____

_____

2. Gross profit ratio

_____

_____

_____

_____

3. Return on total assets

_____

_____

_____

_____

_____

4. Return on common stockholders' equity

_____

_____

_____

_____

_____

5. Basic earnings per share

_____

_____

_____

_____

Analysis and Interpretation:

_____

_____

_____

_____

_____

Part 1

_____

_____

_____

_____

_____

_____

_____

_____

_____

_____

_____

_____

_____

_____

_____

_____

_____

_____

_____

Part 2

_____

_____

_____

_____

_____

_____

_____

_____

_____

_____

_____

_____

_____

_____

Part 3

_____

(1) _____

_____

_____

_____

(2) _____

_____

_____

(3) _____

_____

_____

(4) _____

_____

_____

_____

(5) _____

_____

_____

(6) _____

_____

_____

_____

Hitting the Road—BTN 13-8

_____

_____

_____

_____

_____

_____

Key Figures	Percent	Amount
Cash and equivalents............................		
Accounts receivable, net......................		
Inventories..		
Retained earnings...............................		
Cost of Sales......................................		
Revenues..		
Total assets..		

(2) Comparisons and comments

_____
_____
_____
_____
_____
_____
_____
_____
_____
_____
_____
_____
_____
_____

Appendix B   Quick Study B-1   *Name* _____

(1) _____

(2) _____

(3) _____

(4) _____

Quick Study B-2

Annual Rate of Interest _____

_____

_____

_____

Quick Study B-3

Years of Investment _____

_____

_____

_____

Quick Study B-4

Value of Investment _____

_____

_____

_____

Quick Study B-5

Cash Proceeds at Liquidation _____

_____

_____

_____

Quick Study B-6

Amount Willing to Pay for Project _____

_____

_____

_____

Appendix B   Quick Study B-7

Name _____

Future Value of Retirement Program

_____
_____
_____
_____

Exercise B-1

Years Until Payment

_____
_____
_____

Exercise B-2

Rate of Interest to be Earned

_____
_____
_____

Exercise B-3

Rate of Interest to be Earned

_____
_____
_____

Exercise B-4

Number of Annual Payments to be Received

_____
_____
_____

Exercise B-5

Rate of Interest to be Earned

_____
_____
_____

Appendix B   Exercise B-6   *Name* _____

Number of Annual Investments _____
_____
_____
_____

Exercise B-7

Cost (Present Value) of Automobile _____
_____
_____
_____
_____

Exercise B-8

Cash Proceeds from Bond _____
_____
_____
_____
_____
_____
_____

Exercise B-9

Present Value of Investment _____
_____
_____
_____

(1) _____

_____

_____

(2) _____

_____

_____

Exercise B-11

Amount Borrowed _____

_____

_____

_____

_____

Exercise B-12

	Single Future Payment	Number of Periods	Interest Rate	Table B.1 Value	Amount Borrowed
(a)					
(b)					
(c)					
(d)					
(e)					
(f)					

Appendix B   Exercise B-13   *Name* _____

(1) First Annuity:

_____
_____
_____
_____
_____

Second Annuity:

_____
_____
_____
_____
_____

(2) First Annuity:

_____
_____
_____

Second Annuity:

_____
_____
_____
_____

Exercise B-14

(1) Present Value of Annuity

_____
_____
_____

(2) Present Value of Annuity

_____
_____
_____

(3) Present Value of Annuity

_____
_____
_____
_____

Name _____

Total Accumulated in the Account _____

_____

_____

_____

_____

Exercise B-16

Total Accumulated in the Account _____

_____

_____

_____

_____

Exercise B-17

Future Value of the Fund _____

_____

_____

_____

Exercise B-18

Future Value of Investment _____

_____

_____

_____

Exercise B-19

	Present or Future Value	Single Amount or Annuity	Relevant Table	Interest Rate	Number of Periods
(a)					
(b)					
(c)					
(d)					

Appendix C   Quick Study C-1

Name _____

(1) _____
(2) _____
(3) _____

(4) _____
(5) _____

_____

Quick Study C-2

True: _____

_____

_____

_____

Quick Study C-3

GENERAL JOURNAL

Date		Account Titles and Explanation	PR	Debit	Credit

Quick Study C-4

(1)

GENERAL JOURNAL

Date		Account Titles and Explanation	PR	Debit	Credit

(2)

_____

_____

_____

_____

(3)   GENERAL JOURNAL

Date		Account Titles and Explanation	PR	Debit	Credit

Quick Study C-5

GENERAL JOURNAL

Date		Account Titles and Explanation	PR	Debit	Credit

Quick Study C-6

GENERAL JOURNAL

Date		Account Titles and Explanation	PR	Debit	Credit

Name _____

GENERAL JOURNAL

Date		Account Titles and Explanation	PR	Debit	Credit

Quick Study C-8

GENERAL JOURNAL

Date		Account Titles and Explanation	PR	Debit	Credit

Quick Study C-9

GENERAL JOURNAL

Date		Account Titles and Explanation	PR	Debit	Credit

(1)

GENERAL JOURNAL

Date		Account Titles and Explanation	PR	Debit	Credit

(2) _____

_____

_____

_____

_____

Quick Study C-11

1. Return on Total Assets: _____

_____

2. _____

_____

Quick Study C-12

(1) Return on Total Assets—Component Analysis

_____

_____

_____

(2) _____

_____

_____

_____

Appendix C   Quick Study C-13^A   *Name* _____

GENERAL JOURNAL

Date	Account Titles and Explanation	PR	Debit	Credit
	Date of Sale:			
	Date of Payment:			

Quick Study C-14^A

GENERAL JOURNAL

Date	Account Titles and Explanation	PR	Debit	Credit

Quick Study C-15

(1) _____

_____

(2) _____

_____

Quick Study C-16

_____

_____

Name _____

GENERAL JOURNAL

Date		Account Titles and Explanation	PR	Debit	Credit
(a)					
(b)					

Exercise C-2

GENERAL JOURNAL

Date		Account Titles and Explanation	PR	Debit	Credit
(a)					
(b)					
(c)					

Exercise C-3

GENERAL JOURNAL

Date		Account Titles and Explanation	PR	Debit	Credit
(a)					
(b)					

Appendix C   Exercise C-4   *Name* _____

(a) _____

(b) _____

(c) _____

(d) _____
_____

Exercise C-5

(1) _____

(2) _____
_____

(1)   GENERAL JOURNAL

Date		Account Titles and Explanation	PR	Debit	Credit

(2)

_____

_____

_____

_____

(3)   GENERAL JOURNAL

Date		Account Titles and Explanation	PR	Debit	Credit

Exercise C-7

Available-for-Sale Portfolio	Cost	Fair Value	Unrealized Gain (Loss)

GENERAL JOURNAL

Date		Account Titles and Explanation	PR	Debit	Credit

Name _____

GENERAL JOURNAL

Date	Account Titles and Explanation	PR	Debit	Credit
(a)				
(b)				
(c)				
(d)				
(e)				
(f)				
(g)				

GENERAL JOURNAL

Date		Account Titles and Explanation	PR	Debit	Credit

Computation of Fair Value Adjustment:

Securities	Cost	Fair Value	Unrealized Gain (Loss)

Exercise C-10

GENERAL JOURNAL

Date		Account Titles and Explanation	PR	Debit	Credit

Computation of Fair Value Adjustment:

	12/31/2010	12/31/2011
Cost		
Fair Value	_____	_____
Gain (Loss)		

Adjustments:

Appendix C   Exercise C-11   Name _____

GENERAL JOURNAL

Date	Account Titles and Explanation	PR	Debit	Credit
2009:				
2010:				
2011:				
2012:				

Supporting Computations:

(1) Classification of Investments

(a)
_____

_____

(b)
_____

_____

(c)
_____

_____

_____

(d)
_____

_____

(e)
_____

_____

_____

(2)   **GENERAL JOURNAL**

Date	Account Titles and Explanation	PR	Debit	Credit

Computation of Fair Value Adjustment:

Long-Term AFS Securities	Cost	Fair Value

Name _____

GENERAL JOURNAL

Date	Account Titles and Explanation	PR	Debit	Credit
2011:				
2012:				

2011 Return on Total Assets: _____

_____

_____

_____

2012 Return on Total Assets: _____

_____

_____

_____

Analysis and Interpretation: _____

_____

_____

_____

_____

_____

_____

Name _____

GENERAL JOURNAL

Date	Account Titles and Explanation	PR	Debit	Credit
2011:				
2012:				

Appendix C   Exercise C-16^A *Name* _____

Reported on Quarterly Statement Ended June 30, 2011: _____

_____
_____
_____
_____
_____

Reported on Quarterly Statement Ended September 30, 2011: _____

_____
_____
_____
_____
_____
_____

Reported on Quarterly Statement Ended December 31, 2011: _____

_____
_____
_____
_____
_____
_____

Reported on Quarterly Statement Ended March 31, 2012: _____

_____
_____
_____
_____
_____

Exercise C-17

(1) _____
_____
_____

(2) _____
_____
_____
_____

GENERAL JOURNAL

Date	Account Titles and Explanation	PR	Debit	Credit
2011:				
2012:				

Part 1

GENERAL JOURNAL

Date	Account Titles and Explanation	PR	Debit	Credit
2013:				

Part 2

Date	Account Titles and Explanation	PR	Debit	Credit

GENERAL JOURNAL

Date	Account Titles and Explanation	PR	Debit	Credit

Part 2

Comparison of Cost and Fair Value for AFS Portfolio				
Security	Computations	Cost	Fair Value	Unrealized Gain (Loss)

Part 3

GENERAL JOURNAL

Date	Account Titles and Explanation	PR	Debit	Credit

Part 4

_____

_____

_____

_____

Part 5

Income Statement:

_____

_____

_____

Balance Sheet (Equity Section Only):

_____

_____

Part 1

GENERAL JOURNAL

Date	Account Titles and Explanation	PR	Debit	Credit
2011:				

Supporting work:

Part 1   (Continued)

GENERAL JOURNAL

Date	Account Titles and Explanation	PR	Debit	Credit
2012:				

Supporting work:

GENERAL JOURNAL

Date	Account Titles and Explanation	PR	Debit	Credit
2013:				

Supporting work:

Part 2

	12/31/2011	12/31/2012	12/31/2013
Long-Term AFS Securities (cost)			
Fair Value Adjustment Balance	_____	_____	_____
Long-Term AFS Securities (Fair Value)			

Part 3

	2011	2012	2013
Realized Gains (Losses)			
	=======	=======	=======
Unrealized Gains (Losses) at year-end			

Problem C-4A or C-4B

Part 1

Balance sheet disclosure:

_____

_____

_____

Supporting work:

AFS Securities on Dec. 31, 2011	Cost	Fair Value

Part 2

GENERAL JOURNAL

Date	Account Titles and Explanation	PR	Debit	Credit

Supporting Computations:

AFS Securities	Cost	Fair Value

Part 3

Disclosures:

Stock Sold	Cost	Sale Value	Realized Gain (Loss)

Part 1

(1)   GENERAL JOURNAL

Date	Account Titles and Explanation	PR	Debit	Credit
2011:				
2012:				
2013:				

(2) Carrying Value Per Share: _____

_____

_____

_____

_____

(3) Change in Equity: _____

_____

_____

_____

_____

_____

Part 2

(1)

GENERAL JOURNAL

Date	Account Titles and Explanation	PR	Debit	Credit
2011:				
2012:				
2013:				

Part 2   (Continued)

(2) Investment Cost Per Share: _____

_____

_____

_____

_____

(3) Change in Equity: _____

_____

_____

_____

_____

_____

_____

_____

Part 1

GENERAL JOURNAL

Date	Account Titles and Explanation	PR	Debit	Credit
2011:				

Part 1   (Continued)

GENERAL JOURNAL

Date	Account Titles and Explanation	PR	Debit	Credit
2012:				

Part 2

Foreign Exchange Gain (Loss) Reported:

_____

_____

_____

_____

_____

Part 3

_____

_____

_____

_____

_____

_____

_____

_____

Part 1

GENERAL JOURNAL

Date	Account Titles and Explanation	PR	Debit	Credit

Part 2

GENERAL JOURNAL

Date	Account Titles and Explanation	PR	Debit	Credit

(1) _____

_____

_____

_____

(2) _____

_____

_____

_____

_____

_____

_____

_____

_____

_____

(3) _____

_____

_____

_____

_____

(4) _____

_____

_____

_____

_____

(5) FastForward: _____

_____

_____

_____

_____

_____

_____

_____

_____

Appendix C   Comparative Analysis   *Name* _____
              BTN C-2

(1) **RIM's Return on Total Assets:**
              Current Year
_____
_____
_____
              Prior Year
_____
_____

       Apple's Return on Total Assets:
              Current Year
_____
_____
_____
              Prior Year
_____
_____
_____

(2) **RIM's Component Analysis of Return on Total Assets:**
              Current Year
_____
_____
_____
              Prior Year
_____
_____
_____

       Apple's Component Analysis of Return on Total Assets:
              Current Year
_____
_____
_____
              Prior Year
_____
_____
_____

(3) Current Year Analysis: _____

_____

_____

_____

Prior Year Analysis::

_____

_____

_____

_____

_____

Ethics Challenge—BTN C-3

(1) _____

_____

_____

_____

_____

_____

_____

_____

(2) _____

_____

_____

_____

_____

_____

_____

_____

(3) _____

_____

_____

_____

_____

MEMORANDUM

TO:

FROM:

DATE:

SUBJECT:

(1) _____
_____
_____
_____
_____
_____
_____
_____

(2) _____
_____
_____
_____
_____
_____
_____
_____
_____

(3) _____
_____
_____
_____
_____
_____
_____

(4) _____
_____
_____

(1) _____
_____
_____

(2) _____
_____
_____

(3) _____
_____
_____

Global Decision—BTN C-8

(1)   Return on Total Assets:
             Current Year
_____
_____

             Prior Year
_____
_____

      Component Analysis of Return on Total Assets:
             Current Year
_____
_____
_____

             Prior Year
_____
_____
_____

(2) Current Year Analysis:
_____
_____
_____

   Prior Year Analysis:
_____
_____
_____

   Overall:
_____
_____
_____

(a) _____
_____

(b) _____
_____
_____

Quick Study D-2

_____
_____
_____
_____

Quick Study D-3

	Share to _____	Share to _____	Total
Net income			
Salary allowance:			
_____			
_____			
Total salary allowances			
Balance of income			
Balance allocated:			
_____			
Total allocated			
Balance of income			
Shares of the partners			

Quick Study D-4

_____
_____
_____
_____

GENERAL JOURNAL

Date		Account Titles and Explanation	PR	Debit	Credit

Quick Study D-6

GENERAL JOURNAL

Date		Account Titles and Explanation	PR	Debit	Credit

Quick Study D-7

(1)

	Red	White	Blue	Total
Initial investments				
Allocation of all losses				
Capital balances				

(2)

GENERAL JOURNAL

Date	Account Titles and Explanation	PR	Debit	Credit

(3)

GENERAL JOURNAL

Date	Account Titles and Explanation	PR	Debit	Credit

Quick Study D-8

_____
_____
_____
_____
_____
_____
_____
_____

Appendix D   Exercise D-1

Name _____

Part a

Recommended Organization:

_____
_____
_____
_____
_____
_____
_____

Taxation Effects:

_____
_____
_____

Advantages:

_____
_____
_____
_____

Part b

Recommended Organization:

_____
_____
_____
_____
_____
_____

Taxation Effects:

_____
_____
_____

Advantages:

_____
_____
_____

Name _____

Part c

Recommended Organization: _____

_____

_____

_____

_____

_____

Taxation Effects: _____

_____

_____

Advantages: _____

_____

_____

_____

Exercise D-2

Characteristic		General Partnerships
1.	Ease of formation	
2.	Transferability of ownership	
3.	Ability to raise large amounts of capital	
4.	Life	
5.	Owners' liability	
6.	Legal status	
7.	Tax status of income	
8.	Owners' authority	

GENERAL JOURNAL

Date		Account Titles and Explanation	PR	Debit	Credit
(1)					
(2)					

Name _____

(1)

GENERAL JOURNAL

Date	Account Titles and Explanation	PR	Debit	Credit
(a)				
(b)				
(c)				

(2)

Capital account balances:		
Initial investment		
Withdrawals		
Share of income		
Ending balances		

	Share to _____	Share to _____	Total

(1)

(2)

(3)

	Share to _____	Share to _____	Total

(1)

_____
_____
_____
_____
_____
_____
_____
_____
_____
_____
_____

(2)

_____
_____
_____
_____
_____
_____
_____
_____
_____
_____
_____

Exercise D-7

GENERAL JOURNAL

Date	Account Titles and Explanation	PR	Debit	Credit

Appendix D   Exercise D-8   Name _____

(1)

GENERAL JOURNAL

Date	Account Titles and Explanation	PR	Debit	Credit

(2)

GENERAL JOURNAL

Date	Account Titles and Explanation	PR	Debit	Credit

(3)

GENERAL JOURNAL

Date	Account Titles and Explanation	PR	Debit	Credit

(1)

GENERAL JOURNAL

Date		Account Titles and Explanation	PR	Debit	Credit

(2)

GENERAL JOURNAL

Date		Account Titles and Explanation	PR	Debit	Credit

(3)

GENERAL JOURNAL

Date		Account Titles and Explanation	PR	Debit	Credit

Appendix D   Exercise D-10   *Name* _____

(a) Loss computation from selling assets:

_____

_____

_____

_____

_____

_____

_____

_____

(b) Loss allocation

				Total
Capital balance before loss liquidation......................				
Allocation of loss:				
Capital balances after loss............				

(c) Liability to be paid:

_____

_____

Appendix D   Exercise D-11   *Name* _____

(a) Loss computation from selling assets:

_____
_____
_____
_____
_____
_____
_____
_____

(b) Loss and deficit allocation:

				Total

Capital balance before loss.........
Allocation of loss:

_____
_____
_____

Capital balances after loss............

Allocation of _____ deficit to:

_____
_____
_____

Cash paid by each partner............

(c) Liability to be paid:

_____

Exercise D-12

_____
_____
_____
_____
_____
_____
_____
_____

GENERAL JOURNAL

Date	Account Titles and Explanation	PR	Debit	Credit
(1)				
(2)				
(3)				

Supporting calculations:

_____

_____

_____

_____

_____

_____

_____

_____

_____

_____

_____

_____

_____

_____

Inc./Loss	YEAR 1		
Sharing		Partner:	Partner:
Plan	**Calculations**	_____	_____
(a)			
(b)			
(c)			
(d)			

Inc./Loss	YEAR 2		
Sharing		Partner:	Partner:
Plan	**Calculations**	_____	_____
(a)			
(b)			
(c)			
(d)			

Name _____

Inc./Loss Sharing Plan	YEAR 3		
	Calculations	Partner:	Partner:
(a)			
(b)			
(c)			
(d)			

Supporting Work Space:

Part 1

Inc./Loss Sharing Plan	Calculations	Partner: _____	Partner: _____	Partner: _____	Total for all Partners
(a)					
(b)					
(c)					

Part 2

	PARTNERSHIP Statement of Partners' Equity For Year Ended December 31			
	Partner:	Partner:	Partner:	*Partners'* *Total*
Beg. capital balances				
Plus:				
Owner investments				
Net Income:				
Salary allowances				
Interest allowances				
Balance allocated				
Total net income				
Total				
Less partners' withdrawals				
End. capital balances				

Part 3

GENERAL JOURNAL

Date	Account Titles and Explanation	PR	Debit	Credit

Appendix D   Problem D-4A or D-4B   *Name* _____

Part 1

GENERAL JOURNAL

Date		Account Titles and Explanation	PR	Debit	Credit
(a)					
(b)					
(c)					
(d)					
(e)					

Part 2

GENERAL JOURNAL

Date	Account Titles and Explanation	PR	Debit	Credit
(a)				
(b)				
(c)				

(1)

GENERAL JOURNAL

Date	Account Titles and Explanation	PR	Debit	Credit

(2)

GENERAL JOURNAL

Date	Account Titles and Explanation	PR	Debit	Credit

(3)

GENERAL JOURNAL

Date		Account Titles and Explanation	PR	Debit	Credit

Appendix D   Problem D-5A or D-5B   Name _____
(Continued)

(4)

GENERAL JOURNAL

Date	Account Titles and Explanation	PR	Debit	Credit

(1) _____

_____

_____

_____

_____

_____

_____

_____

_____

_____

(2)   GENERAL JOURNAL

Date	Account Titles and Explanation	PR	Debit	Credit

(3)   GENERAL JOURNAL

Date	Account Titles and Explanation	PR	Debit	Credit

(4) _____

_____

_____

_____

_____

_____

Appendix D   Reporting in Action
BTN D-1

Name _____

(1) _____

_____

_____

_____

_____

_____

_____

(2) _____

_____

_____

_____

_____

_____

_____

_____

_____

(3) _____

_____

_____

_____

_____

_____

_____

_____

_____

Comparative Analysis—BTN D-2

(1) _____

_____

_____

(2) _____

_____

_____

(3) _____

_____

_____

_____

(1) Income allocation per original agreement:

	Maben	Orlando	Clark	Total
Salary allowance				
Per patient charges				
Totals				

(2) Income allocation per Clark's proposal:

	Maben	Orlando	Clark	Total
Per patient charges				

(3)

STUDY NOTES
Organizations with Partnership Characteristics

Appendix D Taking It to the Net
BTN D-5

Name _____

(1) _____
_____
_____
_____
_____
_____
_____

(2) _____
_____
_____
_____
_____
_____

(3) _____
_____
_____
_____
_____
_____

Appendix D   Teamwork in Action
BTN D-6

Name _____

(1)

Income/Loss Sharing Plan	Calculations	Baker	Warner	Rice	Total
(a)					
(b)					
(c)					
(d)					

(2) Team members share solutions.

(3) _____

Name _____

(1) _____
_____
_____

(2) _____
_____
_____

(3) _____
_____
_____
_____
_____
_____
_____
_____
_____
_____
_____

(1) _____	(7) _____
(2) _____	(8) _____
(3) _____	(9) _____
(4) _____	(10) _____
(5) _____	(11) _____
(6) _____	(12) _____

Quick Study E-2

(1) _____

(2) _____

(3) _____

(4) _____

(5) _____

Quick Study E-3

(1) _____

(2) _____

(3) _____

(4) _____

Quick Study E-4

(a) _____

(b) _____

(c) _____

(d) _____

(e) _____

(f) _____

(g) _____

(h) _____

GENERAL JOURNAL

Date	Account Titles and Explanation	PR	Debit	Credit

Quick Study E-6

(a)

ACCOUNTS RECEIVABLE LEDGER

Date	Explanation	PR	DEBIT	CREDIT	BALANCE

Date	Explanation	PR	DEBIT	CREDIT	BALANCE

Date	Explanation	PR	DEBIT	CREDIT	BALANCE

(b)

GENERAL LEDGER

Accounts Receivable

Date	Explanation	PR	DEBIT	CREDIT	BALANCE

Quick Study E-7

PURCHASES JOURNAL								
Date	Account	Date of Invoice	Terms	PR	Accts. Payable Cr.	Inventory Dr.	Office Supplies Dr.	Other Accts. Dr.

Quick Study E-8

June	1	
	8	
	14	
	17	
	24	
	28	
	29	

Quick Study E-9[A]

PURCHASES JOURNAL								
Date	Account	Date of Invoice	Terms	PR	Accts. Payable Cr.	Purchases Dr.	Office Supplies Dr.	Other Accts. Dr.

ACCOUNTS RECEIVABLE LEDGER

Eric Horner

Hong Jiang

Joe Mack

Tess Wilson

Part 2

GENERAL LEDGER

Accounts Receivable

Sales

Part 3

Schedule of Accounts Receivable

Name _____

Segment	Segment Income	Average Segment Assets	Segment return on Assets

Interpretation:

_____

_____

_____

_____

Product	Product Sales	Percent of Total Sales

Interpretation:

_____

_____

_____

_____

Quick Study E-12

GENERAL JOURNAL

Date	Account Titles and Explanation	PR	Debit	Credit
(1)				
(2)				
(3)				

Name _____

SALES JOURNAL					
Date	Account Debited	Invoice Number	PR	Accts. Rec. Dr. Sales Cr.	Cost of Goods Sold Dr. Inventory Cr.

Exercise E-2

March 2 _____

5 _____

7 _____

8 _____

12 _____

16 _____

19 _____

25 _____

Exercise E-3[A]

SALES JOURNAL				
Date	Account Debited	Invoice Number	PR	Accts. Rec. Dr. Sales Cr.

Appendix E   Exercise E-4   Name _____

					CASH RECEIPTS JOURNAL				
Date	Account Credited	Explanation	PR	Cash Dr.	Sales Discount Dr.	Accts. Rec. Cr.	Sales Cr.	Other Accts. Cr.	Cost of Goods Sold Dr. Inv. Cr.

Exercise E-5

Nov. 3 _____
     7 _____
     9 _____
    13 _____
    18 _____
    22 _____
    27 _____
    30 _____

Exercise E-6[A]

					CASH RECEIPTS JOURNAL			
Date	Account Credited	Explanation	PR	Cash Dr.	Sales Discount Dr.	Accts. Rec. Cr.	Sales Cr.	Other Accts. Cr.

(a)

ACCOUNTS RECEIVABLE LEDGER

Date	Explanation	PR	DEBIT	CREDIT	BALANCE

Date	Explanation	PR	DEBIT	CREDIT	BALANCE

Date	Explanation	PR	DEBIT	CREDIT	BALANCE

(b)

Accounts Payable					
Date	Explanation	PR	DEBIT	CREDIT	BALANCE

Appendix E   Exercise E-8

Name _____

			CASH DISBURSEMENTS JOURNAL					
Date	Ck. No.	Payee	Account Debited	PR	Cash Cr.	Inventory Cr.	Other Accts. Dr.	Accts. Payable Dr.

Exercise E-9

April	3	
	9	
	12	
	17	
	20	
	28	
	29	
	30	

Exercise E-10[A]

			CASH DISBURSEMENTS JOURNAL					
Date	Ck. No.	Payee	Account Debited	PR	Cash Cr.	Purchases Discounts Cr.	Other Accts. Dr.	Accts. Payable Dr.

(a) _____

_____

_____

_____

(b) _____

_____

_____

Appendix E   Exercise E-12   Name _____

Part 1

ACCOUNTS RECEIVABLE SUBSIDIARY LEDGER

Anna Page

Sara Reed

Aaron Reckers

Part 2

GENERAL LEDGER

Accounts Receivable

Sales

Sales Returns and Allowances

Inventory

Cost of Goods Sold

Part 3

Schedule of Accounts Receivable

_____
_____
_____
_____
_____
_____
_____
_____
_____

Accounts Receivable Controlling Account

_____
_____
_____

(1) _____

(2) _____

(3) _____

(4) _____

(5) _____

Exercise E-14

Segment	Segment Income (in $ mil.)		Segment Assets (in $ mil.)		Segment Return on Assets
	2011	2010	2011	2010	2011

Analysis and Interpretation:

Part 1

				Accts. Receivable Dr.	Cost of Goods Sold Dr.
Sales Journal					**Page 3**
Date	Account Debited	Invoice Number	PR	Sales Cr.	Inventory Cr.

					Sales Disc. Dr.	Accts. Rec. Cr.		Other Accts. Cr.	Cost of Goods Sold Dr.
Cash Receipts Journal									**Page 3**
Date	Account Credited	Explanation	PR	Cash Dr.	Sales Disc. Dr.	Accts. Rec. Cr.	Sales Cr.	Other Accts. Cr.	Inv. Cr.

GENERAL LEDGER

Cash   ACCOUNT NO. 101

Date	Explanation	PR	DEBIT	CREDIT	BALANCE

Accounts Receivable   ACCOUNT NO. 106

Date	Explanation	PR	DEBIT	CREDIT	BALANCE

Inventory   ACCOUNT NO. 119

Date	Explanation	PR	DEBIT	CREDIT	BALANCE

Long-Term Notes Payable   ACCOUNT NO. 251

Date	Explanation	PR	DEBIT	CREDIT	BALANCE

Common Stock   ACCOUNT NO. 307

Date	Explanation	PR	DEBIT	CREDIT	BALANCE

Retained Earnings   ACCOUNT NO. 318

Date	Explanation	PR	DEBIT	CREDIT	BALANCE

Sales   ACCOUNT NO. 413

Date	Explanation	PR	DEBIT	CREDIT	BALANCE

Parts 2 & 3   (Continued)

	Sales Discounts				ACCOUNT NO. 415
Date	Explanation	PR	DEBIT	CREDIT	BALANCE

	Cost of Goods Sold				ACCOUNT NO. 502
Date	Explanation	PR	DEBIT	CREDIT	BALANCE

ACCOUNTS RECEIVABLE LEDGER

Date	Explanation	PR	DEBIT	CREDIT	BALANCE

Date	Explanation	PR	DEBIT	CREDIT	BALANCE

Date	Explanation	PR	DEBIT	CREDIT	BALANCE

Part 4

_____

_____

Trial Balance

_____

_____

_____

_____

_____

_____

_____

_____

_____

_____

_____

_____

_____

Schedule of Accounts Receivable

_____

_____

_____

_____

_____

_____

Part 5

Analysis: _____

_____

_____

_____

_____

_____

_____

_____

Parts 1 & 2

Sales Journal				Page 3
Date	Account Debited	Invoice Number	PR	Accts Receivable Dr. Sales Cr.

Cash Receipts Journal								Page 3
Date	Account Credited	Explanation	PR	Cash Dr.	Sales Discount Dr.	Accts. Rec. Cr.	Sales Cr.	Other Accts. Cr.

Parts 2 & 3   (Continued)

GENERAL LEDGER

Cash   ACCOUNT NO. 101

Date	Explanation	PR	DEBIT	CREDIT	BALANCE

Accounts Receivable   ACCOUNT NO. 106

Date	Explanation	PR	DEBIT	CREDIT	BALANCE

Inventory   ACCOUNT NO. 119

Date	Explanation	PR	DEBIT	CREDIT	BALANCE

Long-Term Notes Payable   ACCOUNT NO. 251

Date	Explanation	PR	DEBIT	CREDIT	BALANCE

Common Stock   ACCOUNT NO. 307

Date	Explanation	PR	DEBIT	CREDIT	BALANCE

Retained Earnings   ACCOUNT NO. 318

Date	Explanation	PR	DEBIT	CREDIT	BALANCE

Sales   ACCOUNT NO. 413

Date	Explanation	PR	DEBIT	CREDIT	BALANCE

	Sales Discounts				ACCOUNT NO. 415
Date	Explanation	PR	DEBIT	CREDIT	BALANCE

ACCOUNTS RECEIVABLE LEDGER

Date	Explanation	PR	DEBIT	CREDIT	BALANCE

Date	Explanation	PR	DEBIT	CREDIT	BALANCE

Date	Explanation	PR	DEBIT	CREDIT	BALANCE

Part 4

Trial Balance

Schedule of Accounts Receivable

Part 5

Analysis Component:

Parts 1 & 3

Purchases Journal								Page 3
Date	Account	Date of Invoice	Terms	PR	Accts. Payable Cr.	Inventory Dr.	Office Supplies Dr.	Other Accts. Dr.

Cash Disbursements Journal								Page 3
Date	Ck. No.	Payee	Account Debited	PR	Cash Cr.	Inventory Cr.	Other Accts. Dr.	Accts. Payable Dr.

GENERAL JOURNAL   Page 3

Date		Account Titles and Explanation	PR	Debit	Credit

GENERAL LEDGER

Cash   ACCOUNT NO. 101

Date	Explanation	PR	DEBIT	CREDIT	BALANCE

Inventory   ACCOUNT NO. 119

Date	Explanation	PR	DEBIT	CREDIT	BALANCE

Office Supplies   ACCOUNT NO. 124

Date	Explanation	PR	DEBIT	CREDIT	BALANCE

Store Supplies   ACCOUNT NO. 125

Date	Explanation	PR	DEBIT	CREDIT	BALANCE

Store Equipment   ACCOUNT NO. 165

Date	Explanation	PR	DEBIT	CREDIT	BALANCE

Accounts Payable   ACCOUNT NO. 201

Date	Explanation	PR	DEBIT	CREDIT	BALANCE

Long-Term Notes Payable   ACCOUNT NO. 251

Date	Explanation	PR	DEBIT	CREDIT	BALANCE

Common Stock   ACCOUNT NO. 307

Date	Explanation	PR	DEBIT	CREDIT	BALANCE

Retained Earnings   ACCOUNT NO. 318

Date	Explanation	PR	DEBIT	CREDIT	BALANCE

Sales Salaries Expense   ACCOUNT NO. 621

Date	Explanation	PR	DEBIT	CREDIT	BALANCE

Advertising Expense   ACCOUNT NO. 655

Date	Explanation	PR	DEBIT	CREDIT	BALANCE

ACCOUNTS PAYABLE LEDGER

Date	Explanation	PR	DEBIT	CREDIT	BALANCE

Date	Explanation	PR	DEBIT	CREDIT	BALANCE

Date	Explanation	PR	DEBIT	CREDIT	BALANCE

Date	Explanation	PR	DEBIT	CREDIT	BALANCE

Part 4

Trial Balance

Schedule of Accounts Payable

Purchases Journal								Page 3
Date	Account	Date of Invoice	Terms	PR	Accts. Payable Cr.	Purchases Dr.	Office Supplies Dr.	Other Accts. Dr.

Cash Disbursements Journal								Page 3
Date	Ck. No.	Payee	Account Debited	PR	Cash Cr.	Purchases Discount Cr.	Other Accts. Dr.	Accts. Payable Dr.

GENERAL JOURNAL   Page 3

Date	Account Titles and Explanation	PR	Debit	Credit

GENERAL LEDGER

Cash   ACCOUNT NO. 101

Date	Explanation	PR	DEBIT	CREDIT	BALANCE

Inventory   ACCOUNT NO. 119

Date	Explanation	PR	DEBIT	CREDIT	BALANCE

Office Supplies   ACCOUNT NO. 124

Date	Explanation	PR	DEBIT	CREDIT	BALANCE

Store Supplies   ACCOUNT NO. 125

Date	Explanation	PR	DEBIT	CREDIT	BALANCE

Store Equipment   ACCOUNT NO. 165

Date	Explanation	PR	DEBIT	CREDIT	BALANCE

Accounts Payable   ACCOUNT NO. 201

Date	Explanation	PR	DEBIT	CREDIT	BALANCE

Long-Term Notes Payable ACCOUNT NO. 251

Date	Explanation	PR	DEBIT	CREDIT	BALANCE

Common Stock ACCOUNT NO. 307

Date	Explanation	PR	DEBIT	CREDIT	BALANCE

Retained Earnings ACCOUNT NO. 318

Date	Explanation	PR	DEBIT	CREDIT	BALANCE

Purchases ACCOUNT NO. 505

Date	Explanation	PR	DEBIT	CREDIT	BALANCE

Purchase Returns and Allowances ACCOUNT NO. 506

Date	Explanation	PR	DEBIT	CREDIT	BALANCE

Purchase Discounts ACCOUNT NO. 507

Date	Explanation	PR	DEBIT	CREDIT	BALANCE

Sales Salaries Expense ACCOUNT NO. 621

Date	Explanation	PR	DEBIT	CREDIT	BALANCE

Advertising Expense ACCOUNT NO. 655

Date	Explanation	PR	DEBIT	CREDIT	BALANCE

ACCOUNTS PAYABLE LEDGER

Date	Explanation	PR	DEBIT	CREDIT	BALANCE

Date	Explanation	PR	DEBIT	CREDIT	BALANCE

Date	Explanation	PR	DEBIT	CREDIT	BALANCE

Date	Explanation	PR	DEBIT	CREDIT	BALANCE

Trial Balance

Schedule of Accounts Payable

Parts 1 & 2

Sales Journal					Page 2
Date	Account Debited	Invoice Number	PR	Accts. Rec. Dr. Sales Cr.	Cost of Goods Sold Dr. Inventory Cr.

Cash Receipts Journal									Page 2
Date	Account Credited	Explanation	PR	Cash Dr.	Sales Disc. Dr.	Accts. Rec. Cr.	Sales Cr.	Other Accts. Cr.	Cost of Goods Sold Dr. Inv. Cr.

Purchases Journal								Page 2
Date	Account	Date of Inv.	Terms	PR	Accts. Pay. Cr.	Inventory Dr.	Office Supplies Dr.	Other Accts. Dr.

Cash Disbursements Journal								Page 2
Date	Ck. No.	Payee	Account Debited	PR	Cash Cr.	Inventory Cr.	Other Accts. Dr.	Accts. Payable Dr.

GENERAL JOURNAL   Page 2

Date	Account Titles and Explanation	PR	Debit	Credit

GENERAL LEDGER

Cash — ACCOUNT NO. 101

Date	Explanation	PR	DEBIT	CREDIT	BALANCE

Accounts Receivable — ACCOUNT NO. 106

Date	Explanation	PR	DEBIT	CREDIT	BALANCE

Inventory — ACCOUNT NO. 119

Date	Explanation	PR	DEBIT	CREDIT	BALANCE

Office Supplies — ACCOUNT NO. 124

Date	Explanation	PR	DEBIT	CREDIT	BALANCE

Store Supplies — ACCOUNT NO. 125

Date	Explanation	PR	DEBIT	CREDIT	BALANCE

Office Equipment — ACCOUNT NO. 163

Date	Explanation	PR	DEBIT	CREDIT	BALANCE

Accounts Payable   ACCOUNT NO. 201

Date	Explanation	PR	DEBIT	CREDIT	BALANCE

Long-Term Notes Payable   ACCOUNT NO. 251

Date	Explanation	PR	DEBIT	CREDIT	BALANCE

Common Stock   ACCOUNT NO. 307

Date	Explanation	PR	DEBIT	CREDIT	BALANCE

Retained Earnings   ACCOUNT NO. 318

Date	Explanation	PR	DEBIT	CREDIT	BALANCE

Sales   ACCOUNT NO. 413

Date	Explanation	PR	DEBIT	CREDIT	BALANCE

Sales Discounts   ACCOUNT NO. 415

Date	Explanation	PR	DEBIT	CREDIT	BALANCE

Cost of Goods Sold   ACCOUNT NO. 502

Date	Explanation	PR	DEBIT	CREDIT	BALANCE

Sales Salaries Expense					ACCOUNT NO. 621
Date	Explanation	PR	DEBIT	CREDIT	BALANCE

ACCOUNTS RECEIVABLE LEDGER

Date	Explanation	PR	DEBIT	CREDIT	BALANCE

Date	Explanation	PR	DEBIT	CREDIT	BALANCE

Date	Explanation	PR	DEBIT	CREDIT	BALANCE

ACCOUNTS PAYABLE LEDGER

Date	Explanation	PR	DEBIT	CREDIT	BALANCE

Date	Explanation	PR	DEBIT	CREDIT	BALANCE

Date	Explanation	PR	DEBIT	CREDIT	BALANCE

Date	Explanation	PR	DEBIT	CREDIT	BALANCE

Trial Balance

Schedule of Accounts Receivable

Schedule of Accounts Payable

Parts 1 & 2

Sales Journal				Page 2
Date	Account Debited	Invoice Number	PR	Accts. Receivable Dr. Sales Cr.

Cash Receipts Journal								Page 2
Date	Account Credited	Explanation	PR	Cash Dr.	Sales Disc. Dr.	Accts. Rec. Cr.	Sales Cr.	Other Accts. Cr.

Purchases Journal								**Page 2**
Date	Account	Date of Invoice	Terms	PR	Accts. Payable Cr.	Purchases Dr.	Office Supplies Dr.	Other Accts. Dr.

Cash Disbursements Journal								**Page 2**
Date	Ck. No.	Payee	Account Debited	PR	Cash Cr.	Purch. Disc. Cr.	Other Accts. Dr.	Accts. Payable Dr.

GENERAL JOURNAL				**Page 2**
Date	Account Titles and Explanation	PR	Debit	Credit

GENERAL LEDGER

Cash   ACCOUNT NO. 101

Date	Explanation	PR	DEBIT	CREDIT	BALANCE

Accounts Receivable   ACCOUNT NO. 106

Date	Explanation	PR	DEBIT	CREDIT	BALANCE

Inventory   ACCOUNT NO. 119

Date	Explanation	PR	DEBIT	CREDIT	BALANCE

Office Supplies   ACCOUNT NO. 124

Date	Explanation	PR	DEBIT	CREDIT	BALANCE

Store Supplies   ACCOUNT NO. 125

Date	Explanation	PR	DEBIT	CREDIT	BALANCE

Office Equipment   ACCOUNT NO. 163

Date	Explanation	PR	DEBIT	CREDIT	BALANCE

Accounts Payable   ACCOUNT NO. 201

Date	Explanation	PR	DEBIT	CREDIT	BALANCE

Long-Term Notes Payable   ACCOUNT NO. 251

Date	Explanation	PR	DEBIT	CREDIT	BALANCE

Common Stock   ACCOUNT NO. 307

Date	Explanation	PR	DEBIT	CREDIT	BALANCE

Retained Earnings   ACCOUNT NO. 318

Date	Explanation	PR	DEBIT	CREDIT	BALANCE

Sales   ACCOUNT NO. 413

Date	Explanation	PR	DEBIT	CREDIT	BALANCE

Sales Discounts   ACCOUNT NO. 415

Date	Explanation	PR	DEBIT	CREDIT	BALANCE

Purchases   ACCOUNT NO. 505

Date	Explanation	PR	DEBIT	CREDIT	BALANCE

Purchases Returns and Allowances   ACCOUNT NO. 506

Date	Explanation	PR	DEBIT	CREDIT	BALANCE

Purchases Discounts   ACCOUNT NO. 507

Date	Explanation	PR	DEBIT	CREDIT	BALANCE

Sales Salaries Expense   ACCOUNT NO. 621

Date	Explanation	PR	DEBIT	CREDIT	BALANCE

ACCOUNTS RECEIVABLE LEDGER

Date	Explanation	PR	DEBIT	CREDIT	BALANCE

Date	Explanation	PR	DEBIT	CREDIT	BALANCE

Date	Explanation	PR	DEBIT	CREDIT	BALANCE

ACCOUNTS PAYABLE LEDGER

Date	Explanation	PR	DEBIT	CREDIT	BALANCE

Date	Explanation	PR	DEBIT	CREDIT	BALANCE

Date	Explanation	PR	DEBIT	CREDIT	BALANCE

Date	Explanation	PR	DEBIT	CREDIT	BALANCE

Part 3

Trial Balance

Schedule of Accounts Receivable

Schedule of Accounts Payable

Sales Journal					Page 2
Date	Account Debited	Invoice Number	PR	Accts. Rec. Dr. Sales Cr.	Cost of Goods Sold Dr. Inventory Cr.

Cash Receipts Journal									Page 2
Date	Account Credited	Explanation	PR	Cash Dr.	Sales Disc. Dr.	Accts. Rec. Cr.	Serv. Rev. Cr.	Other Accts. Cr.	Cost of Goods Sold Dr. Inv. Cr.

Purchases Journal								Page 2
Date	Account	Date of Invo.	Terms	PR	Accts. Pay. Cr.	Inventory Dr.	Computer Supplies Dr.	Other Accts. Dr.

Name _____

				Cash Disbursements Journal				Page 2
Date	Ck. No.	Payee	Account Debited	PR	Cash Cr.	Inventory Cr.	Other Accts. Dr.	Accts. Payable Dr.

Name _____

		GENERAL JOURNAL			Page 2
Date		Account Titles and Explanation	PR	Debit	Credit

Appendix E   Reporting in Action—BTN E-1   *Name* _____

(1) _____

(2) _____

(3) FastForward: _____

Name _____

Part 1

Research In Motion's Revenue on Segment Assets

Current Year—Domestic:

Current Year—International:

Prior Year—Domestic:

Prior Year—International:

Apple's Revenue on Segment Assets

Current Year—Domestic:

Current Year—International:

Prior Year—Domestic:

Prior Year—International:

Part 2—Analysis and Interpretation:

Appendix E   Ethics Challenge—BTN E-3   *Name* _____

(1) _____

(2) _____

(3) _____

MEMORANDUM

TO:
FROM:
SUBJECT:
DATE:

---

(1) _____

_____

_____

(2) _____

_____

_____

_____

_____

(3) _____

_____

_____

_____

_____

_____

_____

_____

_____

(4) _____

_____

_____

_____

_____

_____

_____

_____

_____

_____

Parts 1 & 2

	SALES JOURNAL				Page 2
Date	Account Debited	Invoice Number	PR	Accts. Rec. Dr. Sales Cr.	Cost of Goods Sold Dr. Inventory Cr.

	Cash Receipts Journal								Page 2
Date	Account Credited	Explanation	PR	Cash Dr.	Sales Disc. Dr.	Accts. Rec. Cr.	Sales Cr.	Other Accts. Cr.	Cost of Goods Sold Dr. Inv. Cr.

Parts 1 & 2   (Continued)

			Purchases Journal						Page 2
Date		Account	Date of Invoice	Terms	PR	Accts. Payable Cr.	Inventory Dr.	Office Supplies Dr.	Other Accts. Dr.

			Cash Disbursements Journal						Page 2
Date	Ck. No.	Payee	Account Debited	PR	Cash Cr.	Inventory Cr.	Other Accts. Dr.	Accts. Payable Dr.	

GENERAL JOURNAL   Page 2

Date	Account Titles and Explanation	PR	Debit	Credit

GENERAL LEDGER

Cash   ACCOUNT NO. 101

Date	Explanation	PR	DEBIT	CREDIT	BALANCE

Accounts Receivable   ACCOUNT NO. 106

Date	Explanation	PR	DEBIT	CREDIT	BALANCE

Inventory   ACCOUNT NO. 119

Date	Explanation	PR	DEBIT	CREDIT	BALANCE

Office Supplies   ACCOUNT NO. 124

Date	Explanation	PR	DEBIT	CREDIT	BALANCE

Store Supplies   ACCOUNT NO. 125

Date	Explanation	PR	DEBIT	CREDIT	BALANCE

Office Equipment   ACCOUNT NO. 163

Date	Explanation	PR	DEBIT	CREDIT	BALANCE

Accounts Payable   ACCOUNT NO. 201

Date	Explanation	PR	DEBIT	CREDIT	BALANCE

Long-Term Notes Payable   ACCOUNT NO. 251

Date	Explanation	PR	DEBIT	CREDIT	BALANCE

Common Stock   ACCOUNT NO. 307

Date	Explanation	PR	DEBIT	CREDIT	BALANCE

Retained Earnings   ACCOUNT NO. 318

Date	Explanation	PR	DEBIT	CREDIT	BALANCE

Sales   ACCOUNT NO. 413

Date	Explanation	PR	DEBIT	CREDIT	BALANCE

Sales Discounts   ACCOUNT NO. 415

Date	Explanation	PR	DEBIT	CREDIT	BALANCE

Cost of Goods Sold   ACCOUNT NO. 502

Date	Explanation	PR	DEBIT	CREDIT	BALANCE

Sales Salaries Expense   ACCOUNT NO. 621

Date	Explanation	PR	DEBIT	CREDIT	BALANCE

Parts 1 & 2   (Continued)

ACCOUNTS RECEIVABLE LEDGER

Date	Explanation	PR	DEBIT	CREDIT	BALANCE

Date	Explanation	PR	DEBIT	CREDIT	BALANCE

Date	Explanation	PR	DEBIT	CREDIT	BALANCE

ACCOUNTS PAYABLE LEDGER

_____

Date	Explanation	PR	DEBIT	CREDIT	BALANCE

Date	Explanation	PR	DEBIT	CREDIT	BALANCE

Date	Explanation	PR	DEBIT	CREDIT	BALANCE

Date	Explanation	PR	DEBIT	CREDIT	BALANCE

Trial Balance

Schedule of Accounts Receivable

Schedule of Accounts Payable

(1) _____
_____
_____
_____
_____
_____

(2) _____
_____
_____
_____
_____
_____
_____
_____
_____
_____

(3) _____
_____
_____
_____